Jill Marc Münste

LEOPARD TANKS IN ACTION

HISTORY, VARIANTS AND COMBAT OPERATIONS OF THE GERMAN LEOPARD 1 & 2 MAIN BATTLE TANKS

With a postscript by Danish Leopard expert
Thomas Antonsen

A

K&F Verlag

PUBLICATION

Completed in terms of content: November 2020

Table of Contents

Table of Contents *3*

Foreword *5*

About this book *6*

Approach *7*

Introduction *9*

Historical Subsumption *12*

From "Beutepanzers" to the Leopard 2 – The History of the Main Battle Tank in Germany 12

The inner-Turkish Struggle against the PKK 25

The Breakup of Yugoslavia 25

The War in Afghanistan 29

Coup d'état Attempt in Turkey 2016 30

Turkish Interventions in Syria 30

The Leopard 1 ....*32*

Description 32

Upgrades 33

Users 34

Combat History 38

    Turkish Leopards against the PKK 38

    Leo 1 in Bosnia and Croatia 38

    Leopards in Kosovo 44

    Leopards at the Hindu Kush 47

    Leos in attempted Coup d'état in Turkey 57

The Leopard 2 ....*59*

Description 59

Upgrades 60

Users 62

Combat History 69

Leo 2s in Bosnia 69

Leopards conquer Kosovo 69

Tetovo and Operation Essential Harvest 77

Leopard 2 at the Hindu Kush 78

Leo 2 Tanks during the Coup d'état attempt in Turkey 95

Leopards under Turkish Flags in Syria 96

Conclusion *101*

Postscript by Thomas Antonsen *107*

About the Author, Jill Marc Münstermann *109*

Acknowledgment *110*

Events *110*

Feedback *110*

Sources List *111*

Foreword

It is April 29, 1994, in the late evening. The air is dry; the Mediterranean insect community hums its songs. Over Bosnia, the night prepares its dark cloth. Major Carsten Rasmussen commands the Nordic Battalion as part of the UN peacekeeping mission UNPROFOR; he also is the commander of DANSQN 2, a Danish tank company equipped with the German Leopard 1 DK main battle tank.

What is the first thing that Major Carsten Rasmussen thinks that evening when the call for help from the Swedish post Tango 2 arrives? Tango 2 is under artillery fire – for the 28th time since the start of the mission! Does the experienced officer, who has a long day's work routine in war-torn Bosnia stuck in his bones, look displeased at first into his coffee cup, in which a miserable rest of the brown broth is waiting to be swallowed? Is he thinking of his homeland, of his family?

Major Carsten Rasmussen will soon give the Danish press a reason for very unusual news. I wonder if he is aware of this when he, tired of the attacks of Bosnian Serbs, gives the order to his Leopard tanks to leave immediately for the position of Tango 2?

Before midnight, Rasmussen's tanks find themselves in battle with Bosnian Serb troops. The enemy uses automatic weapons and anti-tank cannons. Even Soviet-made T-12 anti-tank guns fire at the UN troops. Bullets of all calibers rattle the Danish Leopard tanks. And they return fire. Finally, a Bosnian Serb ammunition depot is hit and blows up. For a few seconds, the emerging fireball lit up the night as bright as day. The battle between armored Danish and Bosnian Serb forces, which goes down in the annals of military history as Operation Bøllebank, marks one of the earliest combat missions for the German Leopard 1 – 29 years after the first production vehicles rolled off the assembly line at Kraus-Maffei.

Many believe that the German post-war tank models Leopard 1 and Leopard 2 are condemned to peace service because of their users' lack of war involvement. Only a few know that both Leopard models have enough combat missions to fill a whole book (Exhibit A: this book). In their long history, these German battle tanks have not only become an international success story with numerous foreign customers for the armament companies involved in their development and production. They have also participated in all kinds of military operations within the framework of UN and NATO missions. On behalf of Turkey, both Leo models even undertook missions without a mandate under international law and were also used by renegade military forces for their attempted coup d'état in 2016.

The Leopard 1 and 2 main battle tanks under Danish, Canadian, Belgian, Dutch, Turkish, and German flags underwent a wide range of combat missions in very different scenarios, with varying threat levels, and against other opponents. This book tells the story of the Leopards and their combat history. It is a success story in terms of armaments and economics and a story about billion-dollar deals with numerous countries and about technical achievements in tank development. Above all, it is a story of simple men and women who, far from home, slept, lived, and fought in their Leopard tanks. It is a story of conquest, and military conflict. Of liberation, joy, future. But also a story of sweat, tears, suffering... and death.

This is the story of the combat missions of the main battle tanks Leopard 1 and Leopard 2.

About this book

Those who want to learn more about the development and technical aspects of Leopard 1 and Leopard 2 tanks can already fall back on a rich selection of specialist publications, even if the mass of available literature is outdated and therefore does not cover recent developments as the Leopard deal with Hungary. However, what is completely missing is a complete compilation and analysis of all combat missions of both tank models; if at all, individual works deal with selected combat operations.

This book fills this gap and provides unique insights into the combat history of both Leopard tank models. Besides, it offers up-to-date coverage about the users and all the tank model's upgrades or variants. Further, it tells in short form the history of German tank development. Please note that I will stick to the terms upgrade or variant to describe different modification packages for tanks. For example, the Leopard 1 A3 is a Leopard 1 with the upgrade A3. In German, the term used for Leopard upgrades is Kampfwertsteigerung. The Wehrmacht instead used the word Ausführung.

I base my book on a variety of sources, which I have evaluated according to scientific standards. Every statement in this book is supported by at least one trustworthy source. Nevertheless, one may forgive me for sacrificing one or the other rigid rule of scientificity on the altar of readability and accessibility of the text, despite all the care I take. Thus, I will summarize references at the end of a chapter instead of spreading them over the text, unless I use a quotation or make an utterly adventurous statement. I don't have a professor breathing down my neck, so I can allow myself to play by my own rules. Where the sources are unclear, or sources could give a false picture, I point out. At the end of each chapter, you will find the references with information about the corresponding sources, which works as follows: At least the author or, if this information is unknown, the publishing organization is given, followed by the year of publication in brackets.

The sources list at the end of this book is sorted according to the authors or publishing organizations; each source mentioned in the references can be found there. With the information in the references, you can identify all sources correctly. I will illustrate this with an example from the introduction: When I refer to the text whose author is unknown on the homepage of the German Armed forces association, I indicate this by mentioning the organization, i.e. Deutscher BundeswehrVerband, followed by the year of publication, in this case, 2019b (b, since this is the second DBV publication of 2019 that I use). In the sources list, you find the corresponding entry: Deutscher BundeswehrVerband (2019b)... A source, whose author is known, in turn, is mentioned in the references by naming him or her plus the year of publication. The search for an entry in the sources list works on the same principle. For anthologies, magazines, and the like, I refer to the authors of the individual work and provide the platform on which the text was published in the sources list. When I refer to online sources, I add a link, including the information when I last accessed the source.

If you trust me unconditionally, you can confidently skip the references at the end of each chapter. They do not provide any further technical information on the topic in question but occasionally provide source-critical comments.

German and English language sources are easily accessible for me; for sources in other languages, I used Google Translator and the translation program DeepL. I can't exclusively say that I miss out on the occasional linguistic nuances, right down to aspects of content, although the programs I use now produce excellent results. Please note that I translated this book myself. Since English is not my mother tongue, I apologize for any linguistic flaws.

Now I wish you a lot of pleasure with the reading of my book. I am proud to finally present it to the public after about a year of intensive work.

Approach

In order to provide the reader with a holistic overview of our Leopards and their combat history, I begin with a historical outline of the main influences that have shaped the doctrine of German tank development, from the first thoughts about armored machines in the German Empire to the development of the Leopard 2. Although the Leopard 1 and Leopard 2 found (and still find) numerous international customers besides the German Armed Forces, most of their combat operations were conducted under non-German flags. The origin and advancement of the German armored force were crucial for developing both battle tank models.

Tank units consist of more than just main battle tanks; as a rule, engineers, signalmen, and other units perform essential support tasks within such units. In the following text, however, I will limit myself essentially to the tanks and deliberately exclude the many supporters. It would go beyond any scope. When describing the combat operations of Leopard 1 and 2, I include supporters if they are of importance for the event described.

The combat operations of both Leos took place very roughly in the context of five conflict zones:

1. The breakup of Yugoslavia, which began in the early 1990s and continued into the new millennium
2. The Turkish Armed Forces' deployment against the Kurdish PKK in eastern Turkey in the early to mid-1990s
3. Then the war in Afghanistan as a consequence of the attacks of September 11, 2001
4. Further, the coup d'état attempt of the Turkish military against the government of Recep Tayyip Erdoğan in 2016
5. And most recently, the Turkish interventions in the Syrian civil war, divided into the Operations Euphrates Shield and Olive Branch

First of all, I will briefly present the conflicts mentioned above. Then I would like to explore our Leos together with you: What can these tank models do? How can their abilities be classified in a present-day context? And what upgrades have been made to keep up with technological progress? I will also examine which international armed forces are among the users of the Leopard tanks. Again I focus on the use as main battle tanks. In the chapters "Upgrades," I present an overview of the different variants of both tank models that have been developed in Germany to meet modern military requirements. Special upgrades for international users only are mentioned in the chapters "Users." A few exceptions, such as the Dutch Leopard 2 A6 MA2, which in turn has an impact on the Heer (= German Army), are treated in the chapters "Upgrades." I also exclude prototypes and test series and limit myself to those variants that have made it into series production. I am sure you will find your way around.

As already mentioned, many publications describe the Leopard family tank's technics very detailed and historically comprehensive. In the sections mentioned above, I will therefore stick to a quick overview of the history of their creation, the background and keep all technical descriptions to a minimum, just enough to be able to fathom the combat operations of Leopard 1 and 2 in their different variants. The motto is: more detailed than a Wikipedia article (and better researched), but shorter than a habilitation thesis. Or something like this. If you want to dive deeper into the historical, political, and technical aspects of the Leopard main battle tanks, you will find enough food in my list of sources.

I consider all this information to be immanent to comprehend the combat operations of Leopard 1 and Leopard 2 described in the heart of this book. In the chapters "Combat History," I take all documented operations of both tank models and describe them as detailed as possible – operation for operation.

If the term "combat operation" is used in respect of main battle tanks, the inclined reader may find manifold pictures in front of his mind's eye. Are you perhaps thinking of old black-and-white photographs and films from the Second World War? Images of massive tank formations colliding with each other until numerous vehicles are left smoking? Do you think of the Iraq War – a conflict that was brought into our living rooms virtually live by the media back in 2003? Do you think of US-American M1A1-Abrams taking apart Iraqi T-55s? In this book, at any rate, I don't limit myself to the full-scale battles in which Leopard tanks were involved, but define as combat operations every contact with regular or irregular enemy forces or every situation that led or could have potentially led to the use of live ammunition.

In my conclusion, I would like to draw your attention to my attempt to evaluate both battle tanks. How do the Leos perform in combat? Do all the superlatives that the press and enthusiastic panzer fans around the globe choose to describe the Leopard 2, in particular, apply with disdainful regularity? In short: Are the Leopards capable of holding their own in combat situations? And should a modern army even think about sending (Leopard) main battle tanks on combat missions anymore?

Please note: I don't think much of translating units, ranks, and formation sizes more often than is necessary for understanding. With every translation attempt, the original's peculiarity is inevitably lost and subconsciously thought of in its English-speaking equivalent. Wherever possible, I will stick to the original terminology and use, for example, in regards to the Danish Armed Forces, of the Oberstløjtnant instead of the Lieutenant Colonel, or the Panzerzug as the smallest formation size of the German tank force instead of making a tank troop out of it. On page 40 (from "**note**" in bold), I give an overview of the terms used in the different armed forces I use in this book. When I speak about soldiers, I always mention the rank he or she held at the time of the events.

Introduction

"40 Years of Leopard 2" headlined numerous media and interest groups at the end of 2019, including the association of the German Armed Forces (Deutscher BundeswehrVerband, 2019b; own translation). However, "40 Years of Leopard 2" is only half the truth, since the year 1979 simply marks the handover of the first Leo 2 tank to the Bundeswehr – the German Armed Forces. The development history of this main battle tank logically goes back much further, namely at least to the year 1970, when the starting signal was given for the development of the Leopard 2.

The Leopard 1, which several armies are still using today, is even a true-to-life senior among present-day main battle tanks – the first series-production model was handed over to the German Army in 1965. And yet, the Leo 2 and its older brother are still relevant – a look at Krauss-Maffei Wegmann's website makes this clear since the Leopard 1 A5 is even advertised there alongside the Leopard 2.

Less than two decades after the end of the Second World War, the development of the Leopard 1 and shortly after that of the Leopard 2 were significantly influenced by the experiences of that very global conflict. The great panzer battles on the Eastern and Western fronts and their image-rich exploitation by Goebbel's propaganda shaped the main battle tank's image far beyond the end of the war. With relevant films and video games such as World of Tanks, the tank has finally arrived in the pop-cultural realm. Even laypeople should be familiar with the most common tank models from the World War: the M4 Sherman, the Soviet T-34, and of course, the Panzer VI Tiger. They fall victim to an agitation that is still reverberating today, putting the tank in the center of the battle on the ground. In reality, the degree of motorization of the German Army was low. At the beginning of the war, it consisted of 90 percent infantry divisions, and the good old horse was still a common means of transportation. Neither during the invasion of Poland in 1939 nor later on the Eastern and Western fronts did the German panzer forces bear the fighting's main burden. Nevertheless, even the engineers involved in the development of the Leopard 2 were probably not free of the described reception of main battle tanks shaped in World War 2 and further stylized ever since. The Leo engineers and their political and military clients indeed had mass tank battles against the hordes of the Warsaw Pact in mind.

Things turned out differently. The Soviet Union dissolution took place in 1991, and the danger of a conventional war in the heart of Europe seemed to be banished overnight. The Leopard 2 celebrated its 12th birthday in that year, the Leopard 1 already its 26th anniversary. At that time, both models had not yet seen any action.

Only a few years later, this should change at least for the Leopard 1. It received its baptism of fire, possibly under the Turkish flag, when Ankara used tanks against Kurdish insurgents in Cizre on the Syrian border. A little later, Denmark sent Leopard 1 tanks to Bosnia, where they soon became involved in firefights with Bosnian Serb troops.

The Leopard 2, on the other hand, had to wait until the turn of the year 1995/1996 for its first combat deployment, when the Dutch used it for the first time outside of maneuvers as part of the IFOR mission in Bosnia and Herzegovina. But as with the Leo 1 in Turkey, this was done under entirely different circumstances than initially thought. Instead of engaging in conventional battles against enemy tanks, the crews of the deployed Leopard 2 in the IFOR mission were faced with security tasks in a civil war scenario. A few years later, German Leopards also operated under similar circumstances in the KFOR mission in Kosovo. The fathers of the Leopard 2 had probably thought more of Russian tanks as opponents than of a yellow Lada. The same applies to Afghanistan, where both Leopard models were deployed in the new millennium. Military conflicts are changing, and with them, the requirements on weapon systems. That is why Krauss-Maffei Wegmann (initially Krauss-Maffei until 1999), acting as the general contractor, is attempting to keep its aging tank models up-to-date for modern warfare with numerous combat upgrade packages and special variants.

It will probably not surprise you that our Leopards have undergone most of their combat operations under non-German flags. Prof. Sönke Neitzel, during a panel discussion of the foundations of the Sparkasse Leipzig in 2018, stated in a somewhat exaggerated remark that the Bundeswehr would be secretly reduced to the performance level of a Volkssturm. In this context, he advocated, to be honest, and simply abolish all German combat troops. Germany would not want to use them anyway; then it would not have to act as if, he said. Concerning the Leopard tanks of the Bundeswehr, a particular core of truth cannot be denied. The Bundeswehr had more than 5,300 main battle tanks at its disposal shortly before the fall of the Berlin Wall (i.e., without the inventory of the Nationale Volksarmee (= National People's Army)). Nevertheless, only in one case (if one considers KFOR and the episode in Tetovo as one coherent case) sent the German Armed Forces a small two-digit number of Leopard 2 tanks on a combat mission. Interesting in this context is the dispute between then German Defence Minister Volker Rühe and his predecessor Rupert Scholz in 1996 about the deployment of battle tanks in the Balkans.

However, in Afghanistan, Mali, and other places, the German Bundesministerium der Verteidigung (= Federal Ministry of Defence) did not and still does not deploy its Leopards, although the Bundeswehr was and is confronted with an opponent capable of tearing even armored vehicles to shreds using heavy weapons and explosives. The question, therefore, arises as to why the German Armed Forces, according to its target plan, wants to increase its Leopard fleet to 320 main battle tanks by 2025 if a threat of booby traps and armor-piercing weapons, as in Afghanistan, for example, is not sufficient to order the deployment of the same.

Some of Germany's international partners are less hesitant in deploying their tanks. The Danish and Canadian Armed Forces, for example, have both deployed Leopard tanks in different situations.

With the Turkish involvement in northern Syria, the Leopard 2 recently appeared in another military conflict, after renegade military forces had already used it for their purposes during the attempted coup d'état in 2016. Since the Turkish Armed Forces' offensives in northern Syria, news of heavy losses among the Leopard 2 tanks has been making the rounds. Pictures and videos are said to document numerous cases. Without a doubt, the Leopard 2, which is often mentioned in the same breath as the best main battle tanks in the world, still has a special aura of global dominance surrounding it. For example, Paul-Werner Krapke, one of the fathers of the Leopard 2, writes in his book about the Leo 2, published in 1986, of a far superiority over all other main battle tanks. He describes the model literally as "without competition" (Krapke, P., 1986, p. 47, own translation). Frank Lobitz sees the Leo 2 even in 2009 and in direct comparison to other battle-hardened western tank models still as the "most powerful main battle tank system" (Lobitz, F., 2009, p. 3, own translation) and as a "figurehead of a new main battle tank generation" (Lobitz, F., 2009, p. 8, own translation). And now pictures of destroyed Leos 2 are going around the world. Has that nimbus of superiority rightly been cracked by the Turkish deployment in Syria? Is the Leopard 2 in the 20s of the new millennium still competitive at all? These are also questions that I will approach in this book.

References for this Chapter

See Deutscher BundeswehrVerband (2019b) for the article "40 years of Leopard 2". Further reading: Zwilling (2018a). The Bundesministerium der Verteidigung (2018) provides information on its website about the new Franco-German main battle tank project. Rolf Hilmes (2011) offers in his Leopard 1 guide an excellent and detailed overview of this main battle tank; from his publication, I also took the total number of German MBTs during the fall of the Berlin wall. Compare Neitzel, S. (2018) for his Volkssturm statement. Nicolai Ulbrich (2019) informs on the German Armed Forces' official website about the planned target strength of the German tank force, further complemented by Kohl (2019). See Krauss-Maffei Wegmann (undated, a) for the Leopard 1 A5 web presence at the KMW homepage. The case of Rühe vs. Rupert can be reconstructed by reading the corresponding Spiegel article (1996). For the praise of the Leopard 2, see, among others, Verlag Jochen Vollert (2015), Lobitz (2009), Zwilling (2018a) as well as Krapke (1986) – here, the praises mentioned dominate large parts of the book. However, as with Vollert, it is enough to study the title and the blurb to get a first impression. Interestingly, Krapke's book contains a field report by a tank officer of the troop, who also finds critical words for the Leopard 2.

Historical Subsumption

From "Beutepanzers" to the Leopard 2 – The History of the Main Battle Tank in Germany

Before jumping relatively quickly through decades of tank development in this chapter, following the essential stages of technical, doctrinal, and strategic-tactical development in Germany, I will shed light on the principles common to all main battle tanks. Tank engineers are primarily concerned with each combat vehicle's three fundamental attributes, the relationship between which must be negotiated since they are in conflict with each other. These are **mobility**, **protection,** and **firepower**. A high degree of mobility is at the expense of protection and firepower, and conversely, a strengthening of the latter two attributes makes the tank heavier and thus slower. Just to give you an example: The A1A1 upgrade of the Leopard 1 has been reinforced with additional armor on the turret sides and gun mantlet, which increases the overall mass by the weight of a Black Forest Horse. I'm not an expert on horses, but Google tells me that the animals weigh 700 kilograms, which is about right. Such an increase in weight naturally has a negative effect on mobility.

The invention of the tank and its first appearance on the western front of the First World War in 1916 hit the military actors at a time when the correlation between man and technology was shifting at breakneck speed during the war. Machine guns, airplanes, and the general industrialization of combat had rendered obsolete most of the pre-war considerations of possible war scenarios. The belligerent nations' armies usually ran against almost insurmountable bulwarks of fire and steel with heavy losses and in vain.

Before 1914, there had been no significant efforts to develop tanks in the German Empire, even though all three basic attributes' technological status was sufficiently advanced for this. Few studies on armored combat vehicles, most of which were available as drawing board concepts or more or less mature prototypes, were reviewed more as mobile artillery or transportation devices than as weapons in their own right and were not procured in significant numbers.

At this point, we should not ignore that the rise of a new branch of military service is not exclusively welcomed with open arms, even if its advantages may be evident. Military organizations are social entities in which political considerations, distribution conflicts over funds and prestige, and the preservation of traditions play a role that should not be underestimated. Thus, when the main battle tank's invention soon confronts entire armed service branches such as the cavalry with the question of their very existence, the readers may imagine that not every cavalryman will have welcomed tanks with sheer joy. Such factors, too, repeatedly slowed down the invention and further development of the tank, especially in Germany, as Markus Pöhlmann points out in his comprehensive habilitation thesis on the German panzer force from 1890 to 1945.

The first deployment of battle tanks was thus withheld from Germany's wartime enemies: On September 15, 1916, the British used their Mark I tank for the first time during the Battle of the Somme at Flers. Some seven months later, French tanks appeared on the Western Front's battlefields for the first time.

On the German side, serious efforts to set up an autonomous tank force had only begun a few weeks before the end of the war. Until then, different concepts had often been researched in a less than purposeful manner from different military authorities, respectively branches. A few of these concepts, such as the AV7 or the Leichter Kampfwagen II (= light combat vehicle), reached series-production readiness and were produced in single to double-digit numbers. More important for the German army was the use of "Beutepanzers" (= captured tanks). In November 1918, some 170 captured battle tanks were in service for the German Empire.

A German AV7 tank, here captured by French soldiers and without armament

An evaluation of German combat reports from the first battles with Entente tanks by Markus Pöhlmann showed that the enemy tanks' appearance had not left too much of an impression on the German soldiers – in fact, they are hardly mentioned in those reports. If they are, the tank is often reduced to a bogeyman for morale without real military value. Indeed, numerous tanks of the Entente failed due to technical defects. Occasionally, the advance of the British tank forces caused panic on the German side; whether this was due to the tanks or, more generally, to a surprise attack movement with superior forces cannot be conclusively determined.

The Germans offensively used tanks for the first time during Operation Michael in March 1918, but without resounding success. On April 24, 1918, the first tank battle in history took place at Villers-Bretonneux: a German AV7 met three British Mark IVs. The AV7 crew destroyed one British MBT before their tank was damaged by artillery shelling, forcing them to retreat. At the same time, another AV7 engaged seven British Whippets (light machine gun tanks). Again, one British tank was destroyed, and three were damaged.

With the loss of the initiative in the summer of 1918, the tanks under the German flag were now given the task of fending off enemy attacks and supporting local counterattacks.

Overall, the main battle tank is unlikely to have had any significant effect on the war course – on either side. It was technically too vulnerable, too slow, and was generally available in too small numbers, even on the Entente side. Theoretically, it would have had the potential to roll over machine gun nests and thus achieve breakthroughs into the front lines. Still, this potential was not fully exploited due to a lack of combined arms training between the infantry and the tank crews, technical shortcomings, and a not yet mature understanding of the tank as a weapon in its own right, at least not before 1918, and even in the last year of the war only in rudimentary form, for example in the Battle of Cambrai.

Also, living and fighting in a tank during World War I was an incomparable ordeal. The men rumbled in almost perfect darkness in a vehicle without suspension through the cratered landscape of the Western Front. Simultaneously, in their midst, an engine, as big as a closet, heated the fighting compartment to up to 60 degrees Celsius within a short time. After two hours in such an armored car, the men were exhausted and unable to continue.

An episode from the final phase of the war illustrates these early tanks' technical and organizational inadequacies: on August 31, 1918, Abteilung 1 and 2, equipped with AV7 tanks, were to counterattack British positions at Frémicourt. Of the nine operational tanks, however, one was transported to the home front before the attack began, to be exhibited for propaganda purposes – to make matters worse, the commander of Abteilung 1 went with it. Added to this were technical defects so that in the end, only three AV7s took part in the attack. As they marched into their deployment zone near the front line, the tanks accidentally ripped through a building due to the drivers' poor visibility conditions, burying 30 German soldiers. The attack failed in the end because the infantry lost contact with the tanks. When the AV7s turned back without having achieved anything, they were mistaken for British tanks by their own people and fired on, which resulted in the loss of two AV7.

This episode is symbolic of the lack of orientation for the tank crews, poor coordination with the rest of the troops, technical shortcomings, and organizational fragmentation, which often deprived the early tank force of its potential punch.

In the postwar period, tanks and armored vehicles played a significant propagandistic role in border control conflicts and inner-German fighting, but their real military role was negligible. Freikorps units demonstrably possessed several Beutepanzers, AV7s, and converted radio vehicles equipped with up to 14 machine guns. The Treaty of Versailles prohibited Germany from 1919 from owning main battle tanks or even producing them for export. As a result, all remaining stocks were given away or scrapped.

With the directive of the Chief of Heeresleitung (= Army Command,) for tank training from 1924, tanks were included in the training of the Reichswehr for the first time. The directive decreed that selected officers from all units and garrisons were appointed as tank instructors to trace current developments in the field of main battle tanks and communicate them to the troops. At exercises, own and enemy combat vehicles were to be represented by dummies, and their effects on fighting were to be researched. Nevertheless, the handling of the battle tank weapon system remained a theoretical subject in the first years of the Reichswehr, which was primarily covered by the field of journalism. German and foreign authors argued about the role of tanks in the next war. The Reichswehr observed and encouraged the debate by translating foreign texts and providing resources for German authors, who drew their knowledge primarily from their World War experience and developed concepts based on it. Volckheim, de Gaulle, Fuller, and many others shaped that debate.

The withdrawal of the Military Inter-Allied Commission of Control from Germany improved the chances of the Reichswehr undermining the tank ban of the Treaty of Versailles. The secret armament program of Reichswehr Minister Wilhelm Groener in 1928 was the first to plan with a German tank targeting seven panzer companies in total. The Reichswehr had been approaching various German business companies since 1925 to develop tank prototypes under the alias "Traktor" (= Tractor). Various concepts for medium and light tanks were approved by the Heereswaffenamt (= German Army Weapons Agency) until 1930 and implemented as prototypes. Also, there was secret cooperation with the Soviet Union in aviation, tanks, and gas matters. From 1929, the secret testing and training facility in Kazan (code name Kama) was available for the tank force. German officers were trained there for all crew positions in the tank (driver, gunner, commander, loader, radio operator). Besides, the prototypes as mentioned above and other models were tested there. The knowledge gained in Kazan was used to a large extent in developing the first Wehrmacht tanks.

After Adolf Hitler's rise to power, he promised the Reichswehr rapid rearmament. And he should keep his word. Initially, however, German-Soviet cooperation was probably suspended in the summer of 1933 more for economic-military reasons than for ideological reasons – in the course of the now official rearmament, there was no longer any need to maintain a secret tank base abroad. Markus Pöhlmann sees Kama's value above all in its function as a military and technical network forge and testing ground, rather than a school of tactics. The project showed

14

the Reichswehr, first and foremost, how not to build tanks. All Traktor projects were rejected. Their successors, the so-called "Neubaufahrzeug" (= newly constructed vehicle), were not approved for series production. Interestingly, Germany, probably due to the Treaty of Versailles' armament restrictions, never took part in the excursion into the realm of multi-turret tanks. This concept was quickly discarded in Europe at the beginning of World War II at the latest. The Neubaufahrzeug remains the only German tank that came close to the multi-turret concept.

In the summer of 1935 – the armament and army restrictions resulting from the Treaty of Versailles no longer played a role at that time – a panzer corps appeared for the first time as an independently operating unit in a war game of the Reichswehr. In October of the same year, the first three panzer divisions were established. The idea of an armored force based on speed and firepower, operationally independent of the infantry, had been discussed for years on the German and international stage. Heinz Guderian, who later became Generaloberst of the Wehrmacht, is often seen as the inventor of the independent tank unit. He probably fired this interpretation by his self-portrayal in his autobiography. This portrayal was elevated to a fact for a long time without being put to the test. In his habilitation thesis, Markus Pöhlmann worked out that Guderian was probably the right man in the right place at the right time to promote the elevation of the tanks to an independent arm of the service within the Reichswehr. For that, he took up ideas that had been circulating in the military community for several years. As early as 1934, Oberst von Faber du Faur coined the term "Panzer Division" to describe the tank force's independently operating unit. Before this, Major von Radlmaier had already brought the idea of a combat vehicle division into play in 1929.

It is noteworthy that in the end, the small, long restricted Reichswehr succeeded in setting up independent tank divisions even before the French and British Armed Forces. The production figures for main battle tanks in the pre-war period illustrate the rapid development of the German panzer force: in 1934, 150 tanks were produced, and in the following two years, a total of 1,297 tanks were built. In 1937 and 1938, another 1,821 tanks were produced. Thus, in the last year of peace, the Wehrmacht already had almost 3,300 battle tanks at its disposal – and this only ten years after the tank force had still been a primarily theoretical matter in the German Army! The Waffen SS also began to mechanize their units in 1939. As a result, the Waffen SS were given preference in the equipment with armored vehicles. Hence, the Waffen SS's mechanized forces played a more important role in the war in relation to the Waffen SS units as a whole.

The German Army Weapons Agency saw itself condemned by various constraints to release a tank for series production, the Panzer I, whose readiness for troops and suitability for the front was doubted by all sides. It was armed with only two machine guns, and therefore was considered underpowered, even in later variants. These shortcomings became apparent in the German panzer force's first combat deployment in the Spanish Civil War, where Panzer I, mostly led by Spaniards, were used. Therefore, this model's production was stopped before the war began in favor of heavier tanks: Panzer II, III, and IV.

The most valuable lessons learned from the Spanish Civil War were, in particular, the effectiveness of an air force that supported operational combat on the ground through coordinated point target engagement and the need for radio equipment in every tank. The latter made a significant contribution to the Wehrmacht's tank force's success in the early war years of World War II. In 1939/1940, most of the enemy forces' tanks did not have radio systems, which made command and control in combat considerably more difficult.

On March 12, 1938, the German tank troops took part in the hastily ordered invasion of Austria, which revealed the still young military branch's logistical problems. Operating materials were so scarce that the tankers had to obtain gasoline from civilian gas stations.

In the fall of 1938, German tanks took part in the invasion of the Sudetenland. A little later, the German Army acquired powerful Czechoslovakian tanks, including their production facilities. This was an urgently needed addition to the German panzer force, which at the time of the invasion of Poland had a total of just over 300 Panzer III and IV main battle tanks; Panzers I and II still formed the backbone of the German tank force at that time, and both types were equipped only with machine guns and a 2-centimeter cannon as primary weapons. Thus, in 1939, the Wehrmacht and Waffen SS tank troops were neither up to date nor even equal to their opponents.

At that time, the National Socialists and the Wehrmacht stylized the main battle tank as a symbol of power. The new German panzers were very present in films, novels, and in the press. The tank had finally changed from a weapon of the others to an expression of new German self-confidence.

In addition to the main battle tanks, other armored vehicles have also emerged since the 1920s. These include armored personnel carriers, which served to transport infantry into and in combat, and armored cars for reconnaissance and assault guns and similar vehicles. Above all, however, the assault guns devised by Erich von Manstein, later Generalfeldmarschall of the Wehrmacht, were soon to prove to be an adequate substitute for the scarce main battle tanks. The assault guns were to be produced and used in a more resource-efficient manner, partly because of the lack of a turret. (The terms commonly used for assault guns and other self-propelled artillery are then as now manifold and not selective, which may lead to some confusion. Thus, at times people speak of assault tanks, tank destroyers, tank hunters, etc., and then there are self-propelled guns. For the sake of simplicity, I use the term assault gun for all turretless armed vehicles on tracks and self-propelled artillery) By the end of the war, Germany should produce more than 22,800 assault guns and about 29,500 battle tanks. Also, there were at least 3,200 captured tanks in German service.

First, however, Germany invaded Poland in September 1939, deploying some 3,200 tanks and assault guns. In the two Heeresgruppen (= army groups) that attacked Poland, the so-called Schnellen Truppen (= mobile units; tank units plus motorized infantry units) represented 25 and 40 percent of all deployed troops, which shows that the Wehrmacht and Waffen SS relied to a significant degree on motorized and mechanized forces for this campaign, using virtually all of Germany's available mobile units. The tank force was numerically superior to its Polish equivalent by four to one. Qualitatively the German operational doctrine beat its Polish counterpart, and at least the German Panzers III and IV and the Czech 38(t) were superior to the Polish models. Germany overran Poland within weeks, but this should not hide the fact that the German side's losses were not insignificant. Wehrmacht and Waffen SS lost 224 tanks, among others.

However, the litmus test was about to face the German tank force with the next military confrontation, which was already casting its shadow: France, the British Expeditionary Force, and the Benelux countries assembled 3,874 tanks in the northeast and east of France. In terms of numbers, the French Armed Forces were considered the second largest military power on earth. On the German side, just 2,580 tanks, now organized in ten panzer divisions, were brought into the field for the campaign against France. From a qualitative point of view, it is striking that the French still regarded their tanks primarily as infantry supporters and therefore had hardly set up any autonomous tank formations. On the other hand, the Germans were able to compensate for their numerical inferiority thanks to superior command tactics, war experience from Poland, and better communication means.

The attack began on May 10, 1940, and the campaign was to last only about six weeks before France capitulated. The German panzer units advanced at an unprecedented speed, the old battlefields of the First World War rushing by. Seized by the flush of victory and supplied with the drug Pervitin (Pöhlmann, M., 2016, p. 317), many mobile units developed a momentum of their own. They hurried away from the majority of the troops storming from victory to victory regardless of losses or the general strategic situation. Therefore, some historians interpret Hitler's infamous order to stop before Dunkirk on May 24, 1940, as an attempt to stem the loss of control of his mobile units. The condition of the divisions, which had been in combat for a fortnight without any halts, seemed critical in any case. Still, that order also allowed hundreds of thousands of Allied soldiers to flee to England. Finally, on June 22, 1940, an armistice was agreed between Berlin and Paris, marking the beginning of a four-year occupation period for the French. The mobile units, especially the German tanks, together with the Luftwaffe, which was successfully deployed against ground targets, played the decisive role in the victory over France. Depending on the source, the German Armed Forces recorded between 700 and 800 tank losses in total, almost 60 percent of which were attributable to the weak Panzers I and II.

Meanwhile, Germany continued to push ahead with the expansion of its tank force. By the end of the year, the number of panzer divisions had been increased to a total of 20, while at the same time, the structure of the units had been streamlined, and Panzers III, IV, and Czech 38(t) joined the troops in increasing numbers. From January to June 1940, almost 2,000 panzers were produced, which was almost 26 percent of the total number of battle tanks produced up to that time. In addition, at the beginning of the attack on the Soviet Union in the summer of 1941, the German tank force relied to a not inconsiderable extent on captured vehicles – about one in ten tanks could be assigned to this category. In the meantime, the Wehrmacht's campaigns in Scandinavia, Yugoslavia, Greece, and North Africa had opened up new theaters of war. Especially on the latter, large tank battles occurred.

With the attack on the Soviet Union (Operation Barbarossa) on June 22, 1941, the largest and probably most murderous theater of war of the Second World War was opened. At that time, the Red Army had four times as many tanks as the German side, although many were outdated. Besides, the Red Army's tank force was in the midst of restructuring at the time, and the Stalinist Great Purge had left a veritable lack of capable leaders. However, the German tankers were also faced with the new T-34, whose sloped armor made projectiles bounce like tennis balls. As late as November 1941, the Oberkommando des Heeres (= Army High Command of the Wehrmacht) gave the order to develop a main battle tank that would have to be superior to the T-34, which clearly shows how deep the T-34 shock was on the German side.

For months, however, the Wehrmacht and Waffen SS relentlessly pushed deeper into Soviet territory. Only before Moscow did the advance come to a halt. The conquest of the enemy capital was to remain Hitler's dream. As the war progressed, the Soviet Union unleashed its enormous arms build-up potential; the Red Army's quantitative superiority was to choke the German Armed Forces to death slowly.

In the winter of 1941/1942, after almost six months of constant fighting at the front lines, the German tank units were nearly down for the count, completely exhausted and battle-weary. The losses of men and material could no longer be compensated. For example, at the beginning of December, the 10th Panzerdivision had available as many as 16 attrited main battle tanks in total and thus existed only on paper as an armored unit. With other divisions, things did not look any better. By January 31, 1942, Wehrmacht and Waffen SS had lost a total of 4,241 tanks. After the Soviet winter offensive had come to a standstill in late March, all German army groups in the east together had a total of (!) 140 operational tanks at their disposal. That meant that the German tank force was in ruins, and there was no longer any thought of concentrated panzer wedges for operational battle decision-making. The German tank force was never to recover from these losses, and from then on, it was used primarily as a front-line fire brigade in the rearguard battles of the following years.

The German offensives of 1942 ended in nothing, followed by the debacle of Stalingrad.

The year 1943 brought the Battle of Kursk (Operation Citadel) in the summer. The Wehrmacht and Waffen SS attacked the Kursk salient with 2,637 tanks, including about 200 Panzer V Panther, 128 Panzer VI Tiger, and 90 Ferdinand assault guns. About 5,000 Soviet tanks opposed them. Although the German side had scraped together all the available mechanized forces for this operation, the modest operational objective compared to 1941 and 1942 could not be achieved. A suggestive transformation of the German tank force from a carrier of the attack to a supporter of the defense was thus completed. That the German tank force was still superior to their Soviet counterparts in terms of leadership and quality is shown, among other things, by one of the largest tank battles in human history, which took place during the Battle of Kursk: At Prochorovka on July 12, 1943, up to 672 Soviet tanks met about 200 German panzers and assault guns. The encounter ended late in the evening; the Soviets lost 522 armored vehicles, the German side three tanks. However, the glaring disparity is partly because the Germans could hold their ground and thus recover damaged vehicles. Nevertheless, Operation Citadel failed because of the Red Army's tenacious resistance and counterattacks, which the Soviets soon carried out on various Eastern Front sections.

Offensives such as the Operation Citadel or later the Battle of the Bulge were nothing more than the last gasp of a military branch that no longer had the necessary capabilities for such operations. At the same time, the German armaments industry continued to churn out high-quality technologies. The Panzer IV, which was initially inferior to the T-34, was later upgraded to its Soviet counterpart's combat strength. And infamous German battle tanks such as the Panther or the Tiger, whose main armament could penetrate a T-34 frontally at 2,000 meters, and others more, caused real shocks among the war opponents. However, these tanks could not be made available in sufficient numbers.

The Reichswehr, and later the Wehrmacht, had early committed itself to gasoline engines for its armored vehicles, a decision that could no longer be reversed at the latest when the war against the Soviet Union began. Despite all the new developments, the German Army did not manage to install diesel engines in any of its newly developed tanks.

With the Allied landings in Italy in 1943 and France in the summer of 1944, German panzers were massively deployed on these battlefields too. For the battle in Normandy, Germany was able to gather some 1,800 tanks and assault guns. The material superiority of the enemy, which was becoming more and more apparent in terms of personnel, the number of battle tanks, but also in terms of resources and especially in the air, pushed Germany's mobile units into the defensive in the West as well – a combat style that was less suited to them than the attack. Especially in the West, the Allies' control of the airspace became so critical that German tank forces' movements were almost only possible at night or in bad weather. With the massive deployment of Allied ground attack aircraft, the German tankers faced an enemy to whom they were almost defenseless. It would have needed its own strong fighting arm of the Luftwaffe in order to protect the panzers on the ground. Still, since 1944 at the latest, this military branch had only existed in isolated instances and had already been overstretched by the air raid protection of German cities. In mid-1944, the Wehrmacht and Waffen SS had a total of 31 panzer divisions, which had very different combat capacities due to the lack of personnel and material and the constantly deteriorating war situation. Slightly more than 7,100 main battle tanks and about 5,200 assault guns were available at that time.

With the increasing duration of the war, Adolf Hitler, who had neither technical nor higher military training, became increasingly involved in detailed questions of the most diverse armament projects, sometimes imposing abstruse requirements. For example, he forced the Me 262 jet-powered fighter to play the role of a fighter-bomber, even though the aircraft was not designed for it. In the intensifying areal warfare over Germany and in the defensive battles on the ground, a strengthening of the fighting arm of the Luftwaffe would have been much more urgently needed, as Adolf Galland explains in his memoirs. Other sources can substantiate this assertion.

At any rate, Hitler still dreamed of major offensives in which German bombers would smash enemy targets when half of Germany lay in ruins. A similar picture can be drawn for the further development of German tank models. In memoirs, numerous authors agree that Hitler was a man who was very interested in and well versed in armament and technology issues. He considered both the macro level of the overall armament and the micro-level of details such as the thickness of armor and got into the habit of doing interventions through orders. As the war progressed, his ideas took on more and more megalomaniacal traits, which became apparent in projects that were both inexpedient and entirely out of the question, such as the Landkreutzer Ratte (= land cruiser rat) or the heavy panzer Maus (= mouse). On the other hand, Hitler's military merits for the Wehrmacht armament and organization are obvious. To portray him, beyond his criminal ambitions, as a fool who meddled in the work of the qualified generals and officials and thereby lost the war single-handedly, as literature of remembrance often tries to do, is not enough.

However, with the increasing duration of the war and lack of success, it was also Hitler who deposed numerous generals with proven success in leading tank units, which further weakened the German panzer force. Another important figure in the development and production of main battle tanks and assault guns was Albert Speer, who was responsible as Minister of Armaments and War Production from February 1942, and the designer Ferdinand Porsche. Both could claim to be in Hitler's favor.

Meanwhile, the agony of the German panzer force continued. Despite steadily increasing production output, the losses could not be compensated for – and not only since the Wehrmacht and Waffen SS fought at least on three fronts simultaneously with the Eastern Front, Italy, and France. Figures from October 1943 on the German tank units' actual strength provide impressive proof of this and underscore the above statement that the tank force never recovered from the losses of the first six months of Operation Barbarossa. Thus, at the beginning of October 1943, the 9th Armee had 16 tanks left, the 4th Armee nine. Other formations were in a similar condition. The year 1943 also represented a new orientation for the German tank force: In February, Hitler brought back Heinz Guderian, who he had dismissed from active service before and, as Generalinspekteur der Panzertruppen (= inspector general of the panzer force), equipped him with broad authority. However, this could not prevent the focus of the armament from shifting further and further away from main battle tanks to assault guns, which seemed more appropriate for defense in the East. They were more heavily armored in the front, had a lower silhouette, and their assignment to the artillery branch contributed to the fact that assault gun crews were excellent shooters. Guderian would have liked to integrate the assault guns into his tank force, but he only succeeded for the heavy assault guns like the Ferdinand.

The Wehrmacht's last significant attempts to win back the initiative failed because of the sheer quantitative and, in part, qualitative superiority of its opponents. Thus the Battle of the Bulge offensive soon got stuck in the winter of 1944/1945 in the massive Allied defensive fire, the lack of own air forces in significant strength, and an acute shortage of fuel additionally hampered the mobile units. Even the heavy tank models like the Panzer VI Tiger II were unable to change these results.

Despite massive air raids by the USA and Great Britain, the German armament industry successfully pushed up its output further. In 1944, it was able to report staggering figures. In that year alone, it produced 55 percent of all assault guns rolled off the assembly line between 1934 and 1945, and in the case of main battle tanks, this year's figure was almost 31 percent. But Germany's armament industry was not able to compete with the industries of Great Britain, the USA, and the Soviet Union at the same time.

The high German output figures for armored military vehicles were also made possible because prisoners of war and forced laborers deported from their home countries had been working in the armament factories since 1940 under conditions that were in part inhumane. In addition, of course, we also have to talk about war crimes. Numerous cases of war crimes have been documented where German tankers participated in. Particularly in the war against the Soviet Union, the political and military leadership fostered and demanded by appropriate orders atrocities against the civilian population and prisoners of war. Especially POWs posed a problem for the Wehrmacht's and Waffen SS's tank forces since they had to assign troops to guard and feed them. But this often did not appear to make sense to the leading players when advancing rapidly under tremendous operational pressure. Following this bitter logic, masses of prisoners of war and alleged insurgents were murdered by members of the panzer force. There is also evidence that German tankers took over logistical and security tasks for murder actions of the Einsatzgruppen (= deployment groups) and committed crimes out of frustration. There is evidence of war crimes committed by the tank force, especially against black French soldiers, and in Italy since mid-1943. With the beginning of the rearguard battles from 1943 onwards, German panzer troops participated in the destruction of infrastructure (catch-word: scorched earth), on the Eastern Front probably systematically, and in France and Italy sporadically.

With the unconditional surrender in May 1945, not only did World War II end in Europe, but the German tank force naturally suffered another deep cut: the Wehrmacht and all paramilitary organizations were disbanded, and the remaining war material was removed or destroyed. As after the last war, Germany was again ultimately without tanks, but unlike 1919, this time no armed forces were allowed at all. Due to the escalating East-West conflict, this was to change more quickly than one might have thought at that time.

First, however, Germany was divided into Allied-occupied zones, from which soon emerged the Federal Republic of Germany in the west and the German Democratic Republic in the east.

The GDR began rearming as early as 1948 by setting up barracked Volkspolizei-Bereitschaften (= People's Police alert units), which was undoubtedly one reason why the West German government under Chancellor Konrad Adenauer had been considering rearming the FRG since the early 1950s. To this end, the widely known Amt Blank was created, which was later absorbed into the Ministry of Defence.

In 1955, the FRG established the Bundeswehr as her new armed forces after joining NATO the year before. I will not discuss the development of the tank force in the GDR at this point, since it had at most a rudimentary influence on the development of the Leopard tanks, as that force that new West German tanks would potentially face.

After the Bundeswehr had been established, procuring large equipment was done in three stages:

1. Acquisition of foreign weapon systems
2. Development of weapon systems by foreign corporations based on user requirements specification made by the Bundeswehr (see HS-30)
3. Assigning German corporations with the development/production

The new German Army's tank force's birthplace is Munster in Lower Saxony, which still plays a vital role in this military service branch today. The Western Allies initially provided around 1,100 M47 main battle tanks for training purposes and several M41 light tanks.

The second stage can be considered a failure, especially with the HS-30. That led to the Leopard 1 being developed into a military vehicle that fits for service.

On the strategic level, it was assumed that in the event of an enemy attack, the Warsaw Pact, due to its numerically superior tank forces, would use wedge-shaped armored formations to achieve breakthroughs at focal points of the front. In this scenario, the German tank force was thought to have the task of conducting counterattacks from the depths into the flanks of broken through enemy tank units in order to bring them to a halt and finally eliminate them.

In 1957 Berlin concluded a military agreement with France on the parallel development of a new main battle tank. One year later, Italy joined in. Among the new battle, tank requirements were a maximum weight of 30 tons, giving preference to the attribute mobility and sufficient NBC protection. For the German tank development, numerous business companies and designers could be won over who had already developed and produced for the German panzer force of the Third Reich, including the design office Porsche and Wegmann and designers such as Rabe, Bode, and many more.

The requirements specification and the development priorities suggest that the decisions made at that time were based on the experience gained during the Second World War. One can assume that the German officer corps has shown certain constancy across the various regimes and epochs. Prof. Robert Citino describes the officers' corps active during World War II as deeply Prussian and draws a line of tradition from the early 19th century to the Wehrmacht. The Wehrmacht campaigns in 1939 and 1940, which were subsequently propagandistically reworked as Blitzkrieg, were not a complete reinvention of the art of warfare, but the consistent further development of the Prussian-German Bewegungskrieg (= mobile warfare) into the age of motorization. This line of tradition of mobile warfare can be seen at least from the Napoleonic Wars on through the stormtrooper tactics of the First World War and into the Second World War. Because the officer corps of the Bundeswehr was also initially based on a significant number of experienced officers of the Wehrmacht, it can be assumed that this line of tradition was at least carried over into the initial phase of the Bundeswehr. However, the question has to be answered as to what extent mobile warfare doctrine still is present after 65 years of the Bundeswehr. This is a research task that this book cannot accomplish. In any case, it is interesting that veterans of the Wehrmacht, and thus men who were clung in that line of tradition, certainly still influenced the development of both Leopard models; after all, even in the year 1970, almost 10 percent of the personnel of the Bundeswehr consisted of former Wehrmacht veterans. According to this, the personal experiences from the war and the general attitude towards the main battle tank's functions and competencies probably played a considerable role in creating the requirements specification initially for the Leopard 1. Also, remnants of the propagandistic transfiguration of the main battle tank may have been anchored in the minds of the first generals and civil decision-makers of the Bundeswehr. When I look at the capabilities and specifications of the Leopard 1, I am overcome by the feeling that this tank is the result of a learning process in which mistakes from the war were identified and tried to be overcome.

As the war progressed, Hitler, Speer, and the decision-makers in the armaments industry gave ever greater weight to firepower and protection attributes. The requirements soon bore abstruse blossoms with absurd projects like the Panzer Maus or the land cruiser P 1,000 Rat.

The decision-makers in the specification requirements for the Leopard 1, on the other hand, gave priority to mobility over the protection factor and thus demanded a 30-ton vehicle. Also, when the Leopard 1 was being developed, it was already possible to penetrate every conceivable type of armor with man-portable anti-tank weapons. This development began to emerge towards the end of the World War. Exempli Gratia, in the night from October 21 to 22, 1944, a single Canadian soldier with his Piat weapon took out a German Panther in Italy – just one of countless examples of a high protection factor overcome with portable weapons and shaped charges. It seemed no longer appropriate to augment armor and, therefore, the tanks' weight, from one type of tank to another and from one upgrade package to another, as the Germans did in the Second World War. The Panzer IV weighed about 23.5 tons, the Tiger 57 tons, the Panther 45 tons, the Tiger II 68 tons; and the tank projects already mentioned, which show certain megalomania, would have exceeded these figures many times over – the Panzer Maus, for example, was supposed to weigh about 190 tons! Interestingly enough, Markus Pöhlmann sees Panzer Maus as the further logical development of heavy battle tanks, and he derives this from their comparable external dimensions. He does not realize that the weight of the Maus almost triples in comparison to the Tiger II, which would have made transport to the front and near front line redeployments almost impossible.

Against the background of the rapid progress on the field of anti-tank weapons, the decision-makers of the Bundeswehr, therefore, asked themselves the question of how much sense it still made to keep increasing the protection factor, which in return always impairs mobility, because more protection means thicker armor means more weight, and not too little, as some examples of upgrades of the Leopards will show.

In addition to a focus on mobility, decision-makers in the Bundeswehr demanded high material preservation characteristics. It should be possible to replace components quickly, and the range of parts used should be as small as possible across different types of the Leopard family. This was probably their way of addressing the chaos of different tank types during the Second World War, which made maintenance, repair, and training considerably very difficult.

Last but not least, it seemed to be of importance to the decision-makers of the German Armed Forces and Ministry of Defence not to continue the policy of the Reichswehr and Wehrmacht of procuring beta products, which suitability for military service was only to be conclusively tested by the troops after delivery of the production series. Retrofitted improvements should then achieve suitability – in the meantime, the soldiers had to deal with their weapon systems' teething problems. The countless variants of all Wehrmacht panzer models bear witness to this practice. Armored combat vehicles such as the Tiger or the Panther were developed nearly without testing rapidly and thrown to the front, where sometimes serious deficiencies came to light. The Leopard 1, on the other hand, was ultimately to go through a development and testing phase of about a decade to deliver a vehicle that was as suitable as possible. The experiences with the HS-30, among others, underlined this decision. The same practice was to apply later to the Leopard 2. It is part of the irony of German tank history that there are now many different variants of both models because the actual service life of the tank models extended well beyond the initially planned period, and the potential combat scenarios have entirely changed in the meantime. By the mid-1990s at the latest, the fight against guerrilla-like operating insurgents replaced the expected mass tank battles of East against West in Central Europe, even though the latter scenario has experienced a kind of resurgence in recent years.

Germany and France each developed their own tank within the framework of the discussed multinational agreement and a standard set of requirements specifications. Comparative tests from 1961 revealed that the Germans had built the better hull, while the French had built the better turret. The solution was obvious, but things were to turn out differently.

Since Great Britain, in the meantime, demanded that Germany contribute to the stationing costs of British soldiers, Defence Minister Strauß bought 1,500 105-millimeter caliber guns plus ammunition from British production. The French only learned of this from the press. The trilateral development was broken off in 1963 and continued separately from then on.

The Germans further developed their main battle tank and designed the turret with the acquired 105-millimeter caliber guns. In 1965, the first Leopard 1 could finally be handed over to the troops after a development period of around nine years, marking the beginning of a great international success story. The Leo 1 initially replaced the U.S. M47 main battle tanks within the Bundeswehr.

Due to various upgrade packages, the Leopard 1 could be kept in the German Army until 2003 and still forms the backbone of the tank force in several armies, as can be read below. Again and again, the tank has won tenders against other models. All in all, the Leopard 1 can be considered as an excellent main battle tank of its time (even if Paul-Werner Krapke, for example, comes to a slightly different conclusion in his book, but in my perception, he seems to be emotionally biased). Finally, the long-lasting interest of non-German armed forces for the Leo 1 underlines a positive evaluation of this MBT. Beyond that, the Leopard 1 was the German panzer equipped with a diesel engine as standard.

Speaking of Paul-Werner Krapke; he is regarded as the father of the Leopard 2, whose development he accompanied as a project commissioner of the Bundesamtes für Wehrtechnik und Beschaffung (= Federal Office of Defence Technology and Procurement), after the graduate industrial engineer had previously been involved in the series production of the Leopard 1 and had worked as a Wehrmacht consultant for the Panzers III and IV.

However, new developments in the military and political fields forged ahead, which led to an increasing quantitative superiority of the Warsaw Pact. The armored forces of the East also upgraded itself qualitatively with tank models such as the T-62. The Bundeswehr was confronted with a scenario in which, in the event of war, it would send its main battle tanks into battle against a vast superiority of enemy tanks, which raised the demand that a "golden Leopard 1" or even a successor would have to have a high first-hit probability at up to 2,000 meters, even at night and out of motion.

The 1963 agreement between the USA and the FRG on the joint development of a main battle tank (KPz 70) was buried in 1970 after seemingly insoluble complications and technical problems. However, the knowledge gained from this project was incorporated into the development of the Leopard 2. At the end of the 1960s, the design office Porsche had submitted ideas for increasing the combat effectiveness of the Leopard 1, which Krapke sees as the birth of the Leopard 2. In any case, since then, the talk has been of the Golden Leopard at the latest. The Ministry of Defence released funds for the development of combat-value-enhancing components for the Leopard 1 as well as components for a new main battle tank by Krauss-Maffei with the participation of Porsche and Wegmann. In the fall of 1970, construction began on 17 different Leopard 2 prototypes, which were then extensively tested, including in Canada and the USA for extreme cold and heat tests. Simultaneously, talks were underway between Berlin and London on a further main battle tank project (KPz 3), which never went beyond the status of concept studies.

While the Leopard 1's protection had to be subordinated to the attributes of mobility and firepower, the Ministry of Defence and the German Armed Forces decided to prioritize firepower for the Leopard 2 under the impression of the Yom Kippur War. The attributes of mobility and protection were set equally ranking behind firepower. In particular, the protection factor should be significantly increased compared to the Leo 1 by enhancing the turret armor. Besides, armor technologies were now available that offer sufficient protection against shaped charge ammunition, so that the "refuge to mobility" (Krappke, P., 1986, p. 54, own translation) no longer seemed necessary. The combat weight of the Leo 2 was to be increased to 55 tons.

The competitive development and tendering of the production contributed to the fact that the procurement of the Leopard 2 neither exceeded the budget (the rational, not the estimated one) nor caused a negative echo in the press. In 1977, the Leopard 2 was close to being ready for series production. The project cleared the parliamentary hurdle. The Ministry of Defence ordered 1,800 vehicles, which were first and foremost to replace the outdated American M48s and the assault gun Kanonenjagdpanzer of the Heer. From the fall of 1978, after almost twelve years of development, the first series production Leo 2s were delivered for testing. On October 24, 1979, the Generalinspekteur des Heeres (= Inspector General of the Army) received the ignition key for the 4th vehicle of the series production, thus officially introducing the Leopard 2 into the Bundeswehr.

In total, 2,125 battle tanks were procured for the Bundeswehr up to the beginning of the 1990s. Leopard 1 and 2 served together in the German tank force before the last Leo 1 was decommissioned in 2003. In 1989 the Bundeswehr counted more than 5,300 main battle tanks, to which the tanks of the National People's Army were added shortly afterward. From the early 1990s, the Treaty on Conventional Armed Forces in Europe obliged Germany to reduce her stock of battle tanks to a maximum of 3,500 vehicles. Today's Bundeswehr's panzer force is miles away from such an order of magnitude; it does not even have 10 percent of its ceiling allowed.

After a massive reduction of the German tank force after the fall of the Berlin Wall by taking out of service all NPA models and the Leopard 1, the German Armed Forces are again planning to slightly increase their Leopard 2 fleet to 320 vehicles.

In his book about the Leopard 2 from 1986, Paul-Werner Krapke considers a successor tank for the year 2000 or later to be realistic or appropriate. Now we are already in the "later" phase. A successor for the Leopard 2 is still to come; the development seems to be at a very early stage. A tank project to replace the Leopard 1, called Panzerkampfwagen 2000, was launched before the fall of the Berlin Wall and, like many other projects, fell victim to the pressure to cut costs and reduce troops. However, the costs of tank development and production multiplied, even when inflation is taken into account. In 1963, the Leopard 1 still cost almost 1,000,000 Deutsche Marks per unit, while the Leopard 2 cost 3.5 times that amount 17 years later. Against this background, the question must be allowed, to what extent a national economy can be expected to develop and procure a new main battle tank.

Since the fall of the Berlin Wall, two basic paths of further development can be observed among the various users of the Leopard 2 as well as among the responsible armament industries: further optimization for the classic duel situation (tank against tank) and a development towards a weapon system optimized for peace missions and asymmetric warfare.

References for this Chapter

The texts by Hans von Seeckt (2013) and Graf Schack (1926) offer an excellent introduction to the dispute over the cavalry's role in future wars. Rolf Hilmes, in his already mentioned Leo 1 guide (2011), gives, quite incidentally, excellent insights into the development of the German tank force after World War II, supplemented by Zwilling (2018a) and (2020); Vollert (2018a) and (2018b), and Krapke (1986), even if the latter work is stuck ideologically in the trenches of the Cold War. Its author appears to be noticeably emotionally affected from time to time. Fortunately recorded on video, Hilmes' lecture from 2016 is a beautiful addition to the publication mentioned above. Markus Pöhlmann's habilitation thesis (2016) may be considered a standard work on the German panzer force up to 1945 and is therefore not missing as a basis for my work. Regarding Adolf Galland's classification of the development of the jet-powered fighter Me 262, I refer to the new publication of his memoirs: Galland (2012) – the original text was first published in 1953. His statements are supported by Wolfgang Ernst's book "War Hitler ein Feldheer?" (2001). I consulted Heinz Guderian's autobiography to further evaluate his significance for the tank force (1994). An overview of Hitler's qualifications is provided by Thomas Weber's "Hitlers erster Krieg" (2011).

To understand how one lived and fought in a World War 1 tank, see Ralf Raths' richly illustrated descriptions (2020a). For characterization of Hitler through the literature of remembrance, see Erich von Manstein's "Verlorene Siege" (1991). Citino's statements about the German officer corps' traditions, which he has worked out in a book, are aptly summarized in a lecture that can be found on YouTube (2010). For further studying, I suggest Isabel Hull (2004) as well as Ralf Raths (2020b). The Canadian soldier who defeated a Panther with a Piat can be found in The London Gazette (1944). Frank Pauli (2010) provides information about former members of the Wehrmacht in the German Armed Forces. In his well-known work, "My Tank is Fight!" (2006), Zack Parsons delivers insights into the obscure tank projects of the German Reich during the Second World War. Nicolai Ulbrich (2019) informs on the official website of the Bundeswehr about the current target strength of the German tank force. The maximum number of Leopard 2 used by the Heer is taken from Althaus (2019). The German Federal Ministry of Defence (2018) reports on its website about a possible successor of the Leopard 2. For more information about Paul-Werner Krapke, see Hilmes (2006). Frank Lobitz informs in his book on the non-German users of the Leopard 2 (2009) about the two development paths observed since the fall of the Berlin Wall.

The inner-Turkish Struggle against the PKK

In order to understand Turkey's military activities from 2016 on, Ankara's perspective on the militant Kurdish Workers Party PKK must be examined, which is classified as a terrorist organization by the Turkish government and many other countries.

The Turkish national state constitution, which came into force with its foundation in 1923, does not recognize the Kurds as an independent ethnic group but establishes the Turkish people as a unit whose language is Turkish. The Kurds are expected to be absorbed by the Turkish people. Between 1924 and 1938, there were numerous Kurdish uprisings in the south and southeast of Turkey. At that time, the government imposed a state of emergency, which was not lifted again until the early 2000s.

The PKK and the Turkish government have been engaged in an armed struggle against each other since 1984, which has already claimed more than 40,000 lives. In the course of the conflict, violent escalation has repeatedly occurred, but there have also been phases of talks, ceasefires, and rapprochements.

At the beginning of the 1990s, a renewed escalation began, leading to the deployment of Turkish Armed Forces in eastern Turkey, with Leopard 1 tanks purchased from Germany also being used against insurgents. The violent clash between the PKK and the Turkish military took on such proportions that Jürgen Grässlin, in his book "Schwarzbuch Waffenhandel" from 2013, calls Turkey a civil war country.

References for this Chapter

The Leopard 1 deal between Germany and Turkey is discussed by Grässlin (2013) and Hodge (2004). Gülistan Gürbey (2014) and Rayk Hähnlein (2018) describe the history of the conflict between the Turkish government and the Kurds; their texts have been published by Germany's Bundeszentrale für politische Bildung (= Federal Agency for Civic Education).

The Breakup of Yugoslavia

What I am here richly abbreviating as the "breakup of Yugoslavia" is, in reality, a sequence of numerous, partly very different, and sometimes only loosely related events that unfolded on the territory of the Socialist Federal Republic of Yugoslavia after the death of Marshal Josip Broz Tito. Those events set in motion a process that led to Yugoslavia's piecemeal dissolution and the founding of numerous successor states. This process was often accompanied by the organized use of force and international interference. Yugoslavia's breakup offers enough material to fill reams of books with it (which has already happened). As I have said, I only summarize here those events relevant to grasp the military background against which the deployment of Leopard battle tanks on the soil of former Yugoslavia took place.

In the early 1990s, multiparty elections were held in Yugoslavia's republics, leading to "nationalist polarization" (Calic, M., 2017, own translation). On June 25, 1991, Croatia and Slovenia declared their independence, and a few months later, Croatian Serbs founded their own state on the territory of Croatia. In January 1992, the Bosnian Serbs followed suit by founding their own state on Bosnia and Herzegovina's territory: Republika Srpska. The result was violent clashes between the regular armed forces of the young states and numerous paramilitary groups.

To bring peace to Croatia as well as Bosnia and Herzegovina, the United Nations decided on February 21, 1992, to send an international contingent of troops as part of the **UNPROFOR** peacekeeping mission. Narrowly defined rules of engagement mostly without any military

25

options for action (for example, UN troops were not allowed to respond to artillery fire by deploying ground forces), a lack of equipment, and escalating fighting between the conflicting parties initially prevented the peacekeepers from making a real difference. In July 1995, the Srebrenica massacre was carried out by Bosnian Serb forces of the Vojska Republike Srpske, the armed forces of the Republika Srpska. UN soldiers watched inactively as some 7,000 Muslim men and boys were murdered under the command of Ratko Mladić. Other conflicting parties in UNPROFOR's area of responsibility (AOR) included Croatia, Bosnia and Herzegovina, NATO, and Serbia.

Also worth mentioning is NATO's Operation **Determined Effort** (December 1994 to December 1995). The Canadian participation in this planned but never carried out operation ran under the name Cobra. The intention was to set up NATO troops capable of advancing into Bosnian territory in an emergency to relieve and extract the UNPROFOR forces stationed there.

With the Dayton Agreement of December 14, 1995, the war in Bosnia and Herzegovina ended. It also marked the end of the UNPROFOR mission. It was replaced by a NATO-led peacekeeping force (initially **IFOR** with about 60,000 soldiers, then **SFOR** from December 1996 and until December 2004) to stabilize the region, initiate reconstruction, and monitor the implementation of the Dayton Agreement. Both missions had extended rules of engagement this time. They can be summarized as follows: IFOR (Operation Joint Endeavour) was to implement peace, and SFOR (Operation Joint Guard and subsequently, Operation Joint Forge) was to stabilize peace in response. Among others, Belgium, Canada, and Denmark sent troops for all three missions mentioned above.

Please note: Events on the territory of present-day Bosnia and Herzegovina often appear opaque; hostilities cannot be clearly assigned to one of the conflicting parties. Therefore I will speak of Bosnian Serbs in a shortened sense, which implies both the army of the Republika Srpska and the Yugoslav People's Army.

In the course of Yugoslavia's breakup, the **Kosovo War** crystallized as another dedicated armed conflict. In 1990 the parliament of the Yugoslav province of Kosovo declared its independence from Yugoslavia. The following year, fighting broke out in Slovenia and Croatia. In 1996, the Kosovar Albanian Ushtria Çlirimtare e Kosovës (= Kosovo Liberation Army), in short form UÇK, made its first appearance with attacks against Serbian institutions. From the fall of 1997, the fighting intensified. The Serbian side sent at times around 50,000 police, special police, paramilitary and military personnel into action. They were under the command of the President of the Federal Republic of Yugoslavia and thus antagonist of NATO and the Kosovar UÇK, Slobodan Milošević. Their goals were the extermination of the Albanian resistance and the expulsion of Kosovar Albanian parts of the population.

In contrast, the UÇK was the Kosovar independence movement's armed arm, which initially consisted of only a few hundred fighters. Still, after its crisis year of 1998 to May 1999, it grew to an estimated 25,000 fighters, most of whom were equipped with outdated hand weapons, while the Serbians disposed of a regular armed force's entire arsenal. In the fighting over Kosovo, there were numerous human rights violations and gruesome massacres (including in Račak), and acts of revenge and considerable damage were done to the infrastructure. Hundreds of thousands of people took flight, triggering a humanitarian crisis that spread to neighboring countries, especially Macedonia. When Kosovo's situation became increasingly critical, and NATO was preparing for military intervention, Milošević initially yielded to international pressure in 1998 and agreed to an OSCE mission in Kosovo. The so-called Milošević-Holbrooke Agreement was soon violated by Serbia, among other things, by the stationing of more than 25,000 armed men in Kosovo. In the first months of 1999, international negotiations finally failed, and the members of the OSCE left Kosovo unobstructed. Milošević immediately ordered a renewed offensive against the Kosovar Albanian resistance with Operation Horseshoe.

Note: In Kosovo, NATO was formally opposed by the Federal Republic of Yugoslavia, which was de facto Serb-dominated. Therefore, in my treatise, I use the terms "Yugoslavian" and "Serbian" synonymously.

NATO decided on a three-phase military intervention with the primary objective of ending the expulsion of the Kosovar Albanian population by Serbian forces, ending the fighting on Kosovo soil, driving the Miloševićs troops out of Kosovo, and stationing an international peacekeeping force. Furthermore, the return of all displaced persons should be guaranteed. These goals were later reflected in UN Resolution 1244 of June 10, 1999, supplemented by other aspects such as the demilitarization of the UÇK (a separate agreement was concluded between KFOR and representatives of the UÇK on June 21, 1999). The minimum goal set by NATO was to minimize the Yugoslav forces' potential for violence.

Phase 1 of Operation Allied Force was intended to combat Serbian targets, while Operation Allied Harbor was intended to provide refugees with humanitarian aid. Finally, with Operation Joint Guardian, better known as the **KFOR** peacekeeping mission, an international peacekeeping force under NATO command marched into Kosovo. This was intended to establish internal security in the country, prevent Yugoslav forces from returning to Kosovo, disarm the UÇK, and provide humanitarian aid. But one thing at a time:

First, NATO naval and air forces bombed Serbian targets in Kosovo and Serbia (Operation Allied Forces) from 24 March 1999, before an agreement was reached 9 June of the same year. As a result, NATO ceased its attacks after 79 days of combat and 37,465 strikes. The German Armed Forces had participated with 14 Tornado combat aircraft for reconnaissance and attacking ground targets, as well as a drone battery. Numerous Serbian targets were destroyed, but the attacks also hit non-combatants. On April 14, 1999, for example, one target turned out to be a refugee convoy. 73 people, including many children, died in the bombing by NATO planes.

In retrospect, it must be stated that the effectiveness of the NATO air war remained expandable. Belgrade's military and police forces knew how to deceive the NATO with dummies and false radio communications and camouflage their positions excellently. Practical cooperation between the UÇK, Albanian troops, and NATO air forces occurred only once, namely during the battles for Paštrik. In return, Sean Maloney attests the bombing a significant psychological effect on the Serb leader Milošević, who appeared increasingly restless and desperate. Operation Allied Forces also marked the first deployment of American B2 bombers. NATO was able to complete the mission without personnel losses due to enemy action.

At the same time, after an internal NATO debate over "boots-on-the-ground" options, the invasion of ground forces into Kosovo was prepared, both in the case of Miloševićs giving in and for a scenario in which Belgrade would remain stubborn. (In this case, NATO assumed that her forces would have to push through Yugoslavia to Belgrade with about 200,000 soldiers, which was unthinkable without the participation of the USA – the Clinton administration, however, hesitated at first.)

NATO planned with five multinational brigades for the invasion of Kosovo. In March, the first units moved to Macedonia. The majority of the invasion troops arrived until early June. Initially, Operation Joint Guarantor Tier 3 was planned for getting the OSCE observers out of Kosovo, who were ultimately able to leave the country unhindered and under their own steam.

Belgrade surrendered on June 3, 1999, believing a NATO invasion was imminent. The Military Technical Agreement between NATO, the Army of Yugoslavia and the Serbian Ministry of the Interior came into force on June 9, 1999. Just one day later, the UN passed the aforementioned Resolution 1244 as the basis for the KFOR mission. Remarkable are the extensive rules of engagement that were part of the KFOR mandate. Lessons had been learned from past missions in the Balkans, where the deployed peacekeeping force had had to watch helplessly atrocities committed. According to a precise plan, Serbian forces began withdrawing from Kosovo, and the KFOR forces immediately followed suit to avoid a power vacuum. Thus, from June 12, 1999, ground troops under NATO command marched into Kosovo. In addition to the Bundeswehr, Denmark and Canada also participated in the KFOR mission. The participation of the latter ran under the name Operation Kinetic.

Initially, NATO had about 17,000 soldiers available for the invasion, but the KFOR contingent quickly grew to a total of 57,000 soldiers at times. In addition to most NATO partners, other countries such as Austria and Russia also participated. Five sectors were created, each under the permanent leadership of one NATO country. The disarmament of the UÇK and its transformation into a civilian organization proceeded.

As a result of the war and unexpected outbreaks of violence of all kinds due to the country's complicated political situation, there was (and still is) a major security risk from booby traps, mines, and unexploded ordnances with which large parts of Kosovo are contaminated.

In both Bosnia and Kosovo, NATO relied on heavy equipment. Numerous nations sent battle tanks and other armored vehicles to the Balkans. A military strike by Milošević against NATO troops in Kosovo was also considered a realistic scenario. The corresponding defense plan of the KFOR troops was called Operation Critical Effort, which was later developed into Operation Thunder. A key factor was the deterrence of Belgrade by show of force.

German soldiers for securing and supporting the mission in Kosovo were stationed in **Tetovo, Macedonia**, near the border with Kosovo. Some of the supplies were flown in via Skopje and secured via Tetovo. On March 13, 2001, fierce fighting broke out between the UÇK and Macedonian security forces. A barracks in Tetovo were also fired upon, which was used jointly by the Bundeswehr and Macedonian soldiers. German Defence Minister Rudolf Scharping responded by sending battle tanks and armored personnel carriers to Tetovo while at the same time withdrawing some of the soldiers regularly stationed there.

After Skopje had asked the military alliance for help, NATO's Operation Essential Harvest finally began in Macedonia on August 22, 2001. The goal was to disarm the UÇK in the country. The Bundestag, Germany's federal parliament, passed a resolution on August 29, 2001, allowing the German Armed Forces to participate in this operation.

References for this Chapter

Kriemann's (2019) book and the omnibus with Erich Reiter as editor (2000) are informative about the Kosovo War. I refer to the printed timetable as well as to the articles of Walter Feichtinger and Rolf Clement. Interestingly, this source is, above all, the immediate chronological proximity to the events, which brings the reader closer to the hopes and fears prevailing at the time regarding Kosovo's future and the lasting success of the KFOR peace mission. The website of the Bundeszentrale für politische Bildung is a useful source of background information on the various conflicts that have resulted from the breakup of Yugoslavia, in particular an article from 2017, which does not mention the names of its authors, and the articles by Calic and Fischer (also both from 2017). Besides, I recommend General Klaus Reinhardt's publication on his time in Kosovo (2002), as I do with Grummitt (2020), Eder (1999) and (2019), Kirchhoff (undated), and Maloney (2019). The latter source also discusses Operation Determined Effort, further reading: Government of Canada (2018b). IFOR and SFOR are also covered in SFOR Stabilization Force (undated), an official NATO website. For the Canadian Armed Forces in Kosovo, see Government of Canada (2018a). For UNPROFOR, IFOR, and SFOR, see also Sørensen (2020). Additionally, compare Windsor et al. (2008). Concerning Windsor, it should be noted that the book takes an overly optimistic view of all Canadian activities. Although it is a textbook, its descriptions sometimes drift almost into the realm of fiction novels.

For the episode in Tetovo, see Ralph Zwilling's book (2020) as well as Frankfurter Allgemeine (2001a) and Spiegel (2001). For Operation Essential Harvest, I refer to NATO (2002) and NGO – Die Internet-Zeitung (2002).

The War in Afghanistan

The United States of America reacted to the terrorist attacks of September 11, 2001, with a military intervention in Afghanistan. The Taliban regime there refused to hand over the alleged mastermind of the attacks, Osama bin Laden. First, a US-led coalition attacked Afghanistan in October/November 2001 as part of Operation Enduring Freedom and ended the Taliban's official rule. After that, an international peacekeeping force under the USA's leadership attempted from the end of 2001 within the framework of the UN-mandated ISAF mission (= International Security Assistance Force) to pacify and stabilize the capital city Kabul. Further, ISAF was tasked with supporting Afghan democracy, the economy, and the Afghan security authorities. The ISAF mandate was suggestively expanded to include additional provinces and was finally extended to the entire country in September 2006. The most important national actors on the side of ISAF forces were the Afghan National Army (ANA) and the Afghan National Police (ANP). Resistance, especially from the Taliban, was never completely broken, and any operation outside a base had to be considered a potential combat mission. In purely military terms, the Taliban were mercilessly inferior for the duration of the ISAF mission – at least on paper – but they had numerous advantages to exploit: many thousands of loyal fighters, retreats, and refuges in Pakistan, support from the Pakistani secret service, money from drug trafficking and international donations, support from foreign mercenaries, profits from a flourishing black market, and the fact that the Taliban skillfully used old and new media for their purposes.

Moreover, all too often, the Taliban were in the position to call the shots. They determined if, when, and where the fight was to take place and had the advantage of surprise on their side. ISAF often was doomed to react to Taliban attacks.

The engagement in Afghanistan represents the bloodiest mission in the Bundeswehr history, with 56 soldiers alone killed in action.

Between 2002 and 2011, the Canadian Armed Forces had to mourn 158 casualties in Afghanistan; its participation in ISAF was known as Operation Athena. Canadian troops had been operating under an ISAF mandate since July 2003, after previously participating in the invasion of Afghanistan. Initially deployed in the Kabul area, after July 2005, the Canadians were given responsibility for the security and internal order of the Kandahar Province, which was considered the epicenter of the Taliban's might. In a series of operations, ISAF troops brought the province and the same name's capital under their control. They broke the Taliban's supremacy (including Operation Medusa to liberate Pashmul). Subsequently, the Taliban tried to establish themselves again, especially in the Panjwai and Zhari districts in western and southwestern Kandahar, respectively. The area around Kandahar is considered the Taliban's birthplace and, because of its border with Pakistan, a good base. Canada ended its involvement with ISAF in July 2011.

The Danish Armed Forces have been militarily engaged in Afghanistan since 2002, including in Helmand Province, and remained in the field until the end of the ISAF mission. The mission was terminated in 2014 – without having achieved anything, as many criticize regarding Afghanistan's still unstable security situation. The international mission Resolute Support took over without delay. However, there are also optimistic voices regarding Afghanistan's future. For example, Premier Løjtnant Martin, commander of the last rotation of the Danish tank unit in Helmand, believes that the Afghan security authorities can ensure internal security (Antonsen, T., 2016, p. 139).

In addition to the Taliban, the international ISAF troops in Afghanistan have repeatedly dealt with al-Qaeda fighters, local warlords, tribal leaders, foreign mercenaries, and drug dealers.

References for this Chapter

Poehle (2014) discusses the end of the ISAF mission. Once again, the Bundeszentrale für politische Bildung website proves its value as a source of information with Thomas Ruttig's article (2017) on the history of Afghanistan and Thomas Wiegold's text (2016b) on the Bundeswehr ISAF participation. The United States of America Department of Defense provides an interesting assessment of Afghanistan's situation (2014). Specific parts of ISAF are discussed by Gunther Hauser (2008) and Thomas Frankenfeld (2009). Canada's further engagement is presented by Schulze (2010a) and (2010b) as well as Maloney (2009) and Windsor et al. (2008), and also in Cadieu (2008). Canada's fallen are discussed in Veterans Affairs Canada (2019). For the Danish engagement in Afghanistan, I refer to Antonsen (2016).

Coup d'état Attempt in Turkey 2016

On July 15, 2016, and on the night of July 16, 2016, parts of the Turkish military attempted a coup against the government under President Recep Tayyip Erdoğan. It was presumably attempted by lower-ranking generals; the Erdoğan government accuses Fethullah Gülen of being the mastermind. The coup ultimately failed because of the military's low participation and strong resistance from the population and the police.

Initially, soldiers occupied the Atatürk airport and the two bridges over the Bosporus in Istanbul, among other places. In Ankara, the police headquarters were attacked, and the parliament building bombed. Then the putschists took control of the state television station TRT and had prepared statements readout. President Erdoğan called on the population to resist at around 23:30 hrs In Ankara and Istanbul; skirmishes broke out during the night between the army on one side and the police and civilians on the other. In some places, the military fired on unarmed demonstrators. Soldiers who had refused to support the coup were also murdered sporadically. Helicopters and fighter jets patrolled the airspace. Until dawn, police and Erdoğan supporters gained the upper hand, and the putschists finally surrendered.

At least 290 people were killed and more than 1,400 injured in the attempted coup.

References for this Chapter

On the coup attempt, see Gottschlich (2016) as well as Tagesschau (2016) and Kröning (2016).

Turkish Interventions in Syria

In her text "Der Kurdenkonflikt" from 2014, Dr. Gülistan Gürbey considers the situation of the Kurds in Turkey to have improved considerably in the meantime. Still, the last few years have probably contributed to a worsening of the situation again. Against the background that of the estimated 30 million Kurds in the Middle East, about 15 million live in Turkey alone, there is considerable potential for conflict on a transnational scale, as demonstrated by the recent escalation in eastern Turkey and northern Syria. However, it is challenging to write about Turkish military interventions in Syria than about NATO and UN missions in the Balkans or Afghanistan. On the information level, a struggle for the prerogative of interpretation occurs with all the means of modern communication technologies, making it not easy at all to process the events with factual accuracy. The fact that Western states with their mostly free media and democratic standards of transparency are accompanying this conflict from the sidelines at most, and that instead states with authoritarian traits and a limited press, such as Turkey and Russia, as well as terrorist organizations and unofficial militias, are the belligerents, does not contribute to objectification. Moreover, I cannot and do not want to treat the entire Syrian civil war in this book, which must indeed be considered the central pivot of most military conflicts in this region. This very conflict also crosses the borders of Syria's neighbors.

In the civil war in Syria, the Syrian-Kurdish militia Yekîneyên Parastina Gel (YPG; = People's Protection Units) achieved military success against the so-called Islamic State (IS). The resulting increase in power for the Kurdish superstructure PYD with the creation of a de facto autonomous Kurdish territory in northern Syria and northern Iraq was and is perceived by Turkey as an immense challenge to its security.

With the operation Fırat Kalkanı Harekâtı (Euphrates Shield), Turkish troops intervened in northern Syria from August 24, 2016, to prevent the establishment of an autonomous Kurdish zone. Ankara itself gave as a reason for the fight against the so-called Islamic State of Iraq and Syria (ISIS). In fact, radical Islamists carried out two devastating attacks on Turkish soil in June, killing more than 100 people. Simultaneously with the start of military operations, suspected Kurdish militant bases on Turkish territory were attacked by the Turkish Armed Forces.

The main burden of the fighting in Operation Euphrates Shield was borne by the Free Syrian Army (FSA), which appeared as Ankara's ally as an alliance of various rebel groups. The Turkish Armed Forces provided support by specialized forces such as engineers, the air force, or even main battle tank units, but had to intervene more and more in the fighting as the offensive progressed.

In mid-October, the campaign to conquer al Babs began. While the warriors of the IS had previously avoided the battle, they now offered bitter resistance. Attempts by the FSA to break through the IS positions at al Bab from the north failed so that the FSA began to encircle the city to the west. Turkish forces then participated in the main push on the city. By mid-February, the Turks had suffered more than 60 casualties, most of which fell during the al Bab offensive. Only at this time could the city be completely conquered. Intervention by Russia prevented the regular Syrian Armed Forces from directly encountering Turkish or FSA troops near al Bab.

According to their statements, FSA and the Turkish Army were able to secure 2,000 square kilometers of borderland by March 2017. On March 29, 2017, Turkey declared the offensive to be over, but repeated battles in the area of operations (AO) were reported even after that.

With Operation Olive Branch, Turkish ground troops and FSA forces again intervened militarily on January 20, 2018, intending to prevent the establishment of a Kurdish self-governing zone on Syrian soil. Prime Minister Binali Yıldırım spoke of a buffer zone 30 kilometers deep beyond the Turkish border. The most important targets of this undertaking were the Kurdish enclaves Afrin and Manbij.

Although the Turkish air force repeatedly attacked Kurdish targets in Iraq, deploying ground troops has so far been limited to Syria.

References for this Chapter

Rayk Hähnlein's text (2018) also provides a rich source for the Turkish military operations in northern Syria. See also Patrick Truffer (2017), Triebert (2017) and Roblin (2019), and Gürbey (2014) for an assessment of the situation of the Kurds from the perspective of 2014.

The Leopard 1

Leopard 1 A5

Description

The **series version** of the Leopard 1 has a combat weight of 40 tons and offers space for four crew members. With a length of 6.94 meters, a width of 3.25 meters, and a height of 2.39 meters, it has comparable dimensions to the Panzer IV of the Wehrmacht. Since the attribute mobility was given priority over the protection factor, the flat silhouette is decisive for the Leopard 1's survivability in battle. The MB 838 CaM 500 10-cylinder diesel engine delivers 830 horsepower and accelerates the Leopard 1 up to 65 kilometers per hour. On the road, a range of up to 560 kilometers can be achieved. The torsion bar running gear used is considered robust and reliable. During the KFOR mission in 1999, Canadian Captain Don Senft saw the Leopard 1 as having a clear advantage over other NATO nations' heavy battle tanks in terms of mobility. This enabled the Leo 1 to reach places that were inaccessible to heavier battle tanks.

The armoring, which consists of welded armor steel, is 70 millimeters thick at the front hull with a slope of 30 degrees. On the sides, underbody, and rear, the thickness is at least 20 millimeters.

For combat, the Leo 1 is equipped with the British 105-millimeter L7 A3 cannon. This armament is able to penetrate the front turret armor of a T-62 at a distance of 1,500 meters. However, to achieve the same against a T-72, the Leo would have to get within 800 meters of its target. An optomechanical target range finder can be operated via the fire control system, which results in an excellent first-hit probability. KE, HEAT, and HEP rounds are available for the main armament; the Leopard 1 can carry up to 60 rounds in the ammunition bunker. An infrared scope has been fitted for night fighting. An MG3 machine gun in the mantlet, which is parallel to the axis of the main gun and quite prone to malfunctions, as well as another MG3, which can be swiveled in all directions as an anti-aircraft weapon, mounted on the turret, complete the Leopard's combat potential. Also, smoke mortars are mounted on the sides of the turret.

It was demanded that the West German tank force's future backbone be easy to maintain – essential assemblies should be replaced quickly. In practice, the engine of the Leopard 1 can be replaced within 25 minutes with the help of a crane. It takes just 15 minutes to remove the barrel and about 30 minutes to remove the complete primary armament. These are absolute peak values; contemporary Soviet tanks have to be shut down for several days to remove the primary armament!

The crew consists of four persons: commander, gunner, loader, and driver. An NBC protection system protects the tankers in the combat area from nuclear fallout, chemical or biological attacks.

References for this Chapter

Hilmes books (2011 & 2016) are indispensable for the technical description of the Leo 1 at the latest. Also, Krapke (1986) knows a lot about the Leo 1. I took the information about the Panzer IV from Alexander Lüdekes Wehrmacht panzers guide (2008). Don Senft's assessment can be found in Maloney (2019).

Upgrades

Starting in 1972, the first German Leopard 1s were modified to the **Leopard 1 A1** variant. This upgrade was used to implement improvements that had already been considered during the development phase but could not be implemented in time for the first batches' mass production. In the A1 variant, the Leopard was fitted with alternatingly sloped armored skirts for improved protection against flank fire as well as against dust exposure. Besides, winterized tracks with upgradeable trackpads were installed, as well as the Waffenstabilisierungsanlage 1 (WSA 1; = gun stabilization system), which significantly reduces the time required for a fire stop. Protective grids additionally shield commander and gunner. A barrel protection cover shields the barrel from weather effects. This upgrade package increases the weight by 1.5 tons. So an Audi A3 was just put on top of the Leo.

In 1975 the Leopard 1 A1 was again upgraded, which led to the **Leopard 1 A1A1.** The shock-absorbing additional armor on the turret flanks, the turret rear, and the mantlet stand out strikingly. The driver was equipped with a passive night vision device and no longer needed to switch on headlights. Furthermore, an additional blackout light was installed. Furthermore, the A1A1 variant comes with the possibility of installing a deep wading shaft of about four meters in height for crossing water. Improved air filters and longer tow ropes round off this variant – the weight increases by another 700 kilograms.

With the 5th production batch, the **Leopard 1 A2** was built between 1972 and 1973, which is equipped as standard with the barrel protection cover, the WSA 1, the armored skirts, the night vision device, improved tracks, and enhanced turret and mantlet armor, which, unlike the A1A1 variant, was not mounted but is part of an entirely new cast turret. The air ventilation system and the NBC protective filtration system have also been improved. Brush-guards protect the smoke mortars; experience from the troops had shown the necessity for this extra.

The **Leopard 1 A3** upgrade was equipped with a welded turret instead of a cast turret for the first time. New storage boxes grant further protection of the turret against shaped charge rounds at the rear. The loader was equipped with a periscope. In addition, preparations were made to install an explosive device for close combat, but its installation was never realized.

Thanks to a computer-driven fire control system (a device derived from the Leopard 2) development and improved observation and targeting devices, the Leopard **1 A4** upgrade package significantly increases the tank's ability to engage targets with precision. Besides, a panoramic periscope has been installed. This variant was produced between 1974 and 1976.

Between 1986 and 1993, 1,225 German panzers were modified to the **Leopard 1 A5** variant by equipping them with a modern FLP-10 fire control system. This included, among other things, a thermal imaging device (from the Leopard 2), a laser transmitter and receiver for exact range finding purposes, and a fire control computer for enhanced targeting. The thermal imagining device gives the tank a significant advantage in night combat over all contemporary Warsaw Pact tank models. In addition, further improvements were made, such as reworking some periscopes, new gear selector levers for automatic gear shifting were installed, and new batteries, new trunnion bearings, an adjustment system, and a cleaning device for the driver's periscope were installed. Arrangements were made to install a 120-millimeter smooth-bore gun – but it was never installed as standard equipment. The headlight was removed from the thermal imaging device.

The **Leopard 1 A6**, which mainly improved the protection attribute, as well as the **Leopard with Smoothbore Gun,** did not reach beyond prototype status.

References for this Chapter
As sources for this section, I used Rolf Hilmes (2011), further Paul-Werner Krapke (1984).

Users

Krauss Maffei-Wegmann assesses the Leopard 1 as a successful product, considering the large number of countries to which the tank was sold, sometimes in considerable numbers. Until today it is still in use in several armies. Probably, for this reason, the Leo 1 A5 is still listed in the product range on KMW's website and advertised as "up to date."

Naturally, the **Bundeswehr** was the first and largest customer for the Leopard 1. In 1965 it received the first tanks of the mass series version. By 1970, 1,829 panzers had been delivered to the troops in four production batches, each with slight modifications. Starting in 1972, these were upgraded to the A1 variant. 1,225 Leos were upgraded to the A1A1 variant between 1975 and 1977. Between 1972 and 1973, 232 vehicles of the A2 variant were produced and handed over. A further 110 main battle tanks were introduced to the troops as Leopard 1 A3 in 1973. From 1974 to 1976, 250 A4 variant tanks were produced and handed over to the Heer. Between 1986 and 1993, a total of 1,225 vehicles were equipped with the new fire control system similar to the Leopard 2 and introduced to the troops as Leopard 1 A5. Over the years, the Bundeswehr procured a total of 2,437 Leopard 1 main battle tanks. In 2003 the last Leopard 1 was taken out of service.

Belgium was the first foreign customer to decide to procure the Leopard 1 (as Leopard 1 BE) as early as 1965. 334 MBTs were ordered and delivered with minimal modifications to the German model (for example, a Belgian secondary armament was installed). From 1974 on, the tanks were upgraded. Among other things, a gun stabilization system as well as a fire control system was added. In 1994 and 1995, 132 vehicles were once again upgraded, including thermal imaging devices, and thus were mainly congruent to the A5 variant. In 2014, Belgium decommissioned its last Leopard 1 and had since entirely dispensed with main battle tanks.

In 1968 both the **Netherlands** (Leopard 1 NL) and **Norway** (Leopard 1 NO) decided to buy the Leo. By 1972 the Dutch Armed Forces had received 468 tanks of the series version with slight modifications such as a different secondary armament. In the 1980s, the vehicles were upgraded to the Leopard 1-V by adding a fire control system. After 1992 the Dutch retired all of their Leopard 1 tanks.

The Norwegians initially ordered 78 tanks of the series version with minimal modifications, such as a modified outside intercom system. At the beginning of the 1990s, the Leopard 1 stock was increased by 92 vehicles from the German Army (59 A1A1 and 33 A5). The vehicles from the 1960s were finally upgraded to the A5 variant and again provided with additional modifications (among other things, the hydraulic gun stabilization system was replaced by an electric turret drive system, an EMES 18 fire control computer was installed, a cover was placed over the driver's visual display unit, and snow-seizing tools were procured). The 33 A5s were also equipped with the electric turret drive system and designated as Leopard 1 A5 NO2. The other Norwegian Leos were then called A5 NO1; they differed by the turret's add-on armor. The first Leopard 1s were taken out of service in 2001, the last ones followed at the beginning of the 2010s.

In the early 1970s, **Italy** ordered 800 Leopard 1 main battle tanks of the series version or the A2 variant (as Leopard 1 IT), after attempts to develop her own main battle tank had also failed after the failure of the trilateral tank project. In 1977 a further 120 vehicles of the A2 variant were procured. From 1983 onwards, the entire Italian Leopard 1 fleet was upgraded to A2. From the mid-1990s, the Italian Armed Forces procured 120 turrets of German Leopard 1 A5 tanks and mounted them on their vehicles. In the meantime, Italy has decommissioned its Leopard 1 fleet.

In 1974, **Denmark** ordered 120 tanks congruent to the A3 variant (as Leopard 1 DK; Danish designation; Kampvogn Leopard 1 A3) as a replacement for the aging Centurion Mk.5 fleet. The tanks were assigned to the Jydske Division (in three brigades of 40 vehicles each). They were fitted with minor modifications to the German standard: Windshield wipers and washer for the driver's periscope, preparations for accommodating US-build radios, an infrared night vision periscope for the commander, modifications to the electronics, a modified outside intercom system, and a few more detail changes. The breech block of the main armament was decorated with a monogram of Queen Margarethe II. As a secondary armament, the Danes kept the MG3.

One Leo 1 leased from the Bundeswehr was made available as early as 1975, and the first tanks produced for Denmark arrived in 1976. In 1978 about 40 dozer blades were procured (various expansions for the dozer blades were purchased from 1981 onwards). The Danes had experimented with different fabric mats as camouflage cover to reduce thermal radiation since 1981. At the end of the 1980s, such mats were procured for the entire Leopard fleet.

In 1988, the Danish Ministry of Defence decided to purchase 110 additional Leopard 1 (100 A3 and 10 A4) from Germany – in total, the entire Danish tank fleet was to be uniformly equipped with the Leopard 1 model, so the Scandinavian country planned with a total of 300 Leos in the medium term. The dissolution of the Soviet Union and the obligations from the Treaty on Conventional Armed Forces in Europe caused in the early 1990s that an additional 70 Leopard 1s that had been considered were no longer purchased. Wegmann and Rheinmetall upgraded all Danish Leo 1s with the A5 upgrade package (designation: Leopard 1 A5 DK) and then fitted them with the Danish modifications in Denmark. As a result, the fabric mats were only attached to the hulls of the original 120 tanks. The upgraded vehicles were issued to the troops between late 1992 and mid-1995. From 1994 onwards, Danish reconnaissance units also used the Leopard. For the future UN mission in Bosnia, a searchlight was installed instead of the infrared spotlight to warn that force might be used.

In the UNPROFOR mission, the Danes improvised because the existing fire control computer was not sufficient for the engagement ranges encountered in Bosnia. A computer bought on the free market and equipped with appropriate software increased the engagement range to 9,000 meters. Between 1996 and 2000, 36 Leopard 1s for Balkan missions were equipped with air conditioning and power generator for operations abroad and new radios and GPS; spare road wheels were fitted to the turret or hull front. Tanks with these modifications were designated as Leopard 1 A5 DK-1. One of the tanks remained in Germany as a reference – this is probably why Rolf Hilmes (2010) speaks of 35 Leo 1 A5 DK-1 instead of 36.

RAMTA mine plows were also procured for the UNPROFOR mission. Smaller improvisations such as windscreens for the loader could also be observed in the Balkans. A protective cover for the driver's sight was first implemented on the vehicles in Bosnia, later on for all Leopard tanks in Denmark. Snow-seizing tools for the tracks were also procured, especially for the operations in the Balkans. Danish Leopards were further enhanced with new fire extinguishing systems during their life span and other detailed improvements.

With the Danish Ministry of Defence's decision in 2004, the last Leopard 1 were taken out of service until December of the same year. A few tanks are preserved in Denmark in running condition.

In 1975, the **Australian** Armed Forces ordered a total of 90 Leopard 1 A3s plus decided upon numerous modifications (designation: Leopard 1 AS1). These included equipping a tropical kit for operating the tank in the tropical climate zone, as well as installing a Belgian fire control computer with a laser range finder. Dozer blades were also procured. Around 2007, the decision was made to replace the Leopard fleet with the U.S. M1A1 Abrams. The Australian Department of Defence had 25 Leos disabled for driving and shooting and offered them for sale to private individuals.

Canada decided in 1976 to purchase the Leo 1 in the A3 variant (as Leopard 1 C1), but with many modifications such as a Belgian fire control system with laser range finder and fire control computer, secondary armament from Belgian production, and some more detail changes. Later a heat pointer was retrofitted. A total of 128 Leos were procured, 114 of which were put into active service. Delivery was completed in 1979. 26 vehicles were retrofitted with additional armor in 1978. In 1995 the Department of National Defence approved the Leopard Life Extension program. It included installing add-on armor (MEXAS composite armor) and the procurement of improved ammunition for the main armament. The designation of the tank remained unchanged. Starting in April 1999, work began equipping some Leos with additional armor components for the Kosovo mission. 126 Leos were upgraded with A5 turrets between 1999 and 2001 (as Leopard 1 C2). Also, 26 C2 tanks were again equipped with additional armor and spall liners in 2000, increasing their weight to around 47 tons. In addition, some Leos were modified to operate mine rollers, mine plows, and dozer blades. In 2003, the Canadian Ministry of Defence decided to phase out its main battle tank fleet altogether and replace them with wheeled armored cars. In the fall of 2006, when the last Leopards were about to be decommissioned, Operation Medusa in Afghanistan led to a change in thinking. The decommissioning of the Leos was stopped and partially reversed, Leopard 1 tanks were quickly fitted with additional armor (including new MEXAS composite armor) and sent to Kandahar, and Leopard 2 tanks were leased from Germany in a rush. At the end of the 2010s, the Canadian Army finally decommissioned the last Leopard 1 tank.

Turkey obtained 77 Leopard 1 A3 with some modifications (as Leopard 1 T1) from 1982 on. A laser range finder was installed, and the active infrared system was replaced by the passive targeting and observation device PZB 200. A further 150 Leopard 1 A4s from Bundeswehr stocks were converted to the T1 variant in the early 1990s and delivered to Turkey, before 85 more Leo panzers from Bundeswehr stocks followed in the mid-1990s. German Minister of Defence, Gerhard Stoltenberg (CDU; Christian Democratic Union of Germany), stumbled over the delivery of 150 Leopard 1 because he ultimately had to report that he had delivered the last batch of 19 vehicles. However, the federal parliament had previously expressly prohibited this. According to Global Security, the Turkish Army still has 397 Leopard 1 A3 and A4 tanks in its inventory, which were upgraded with a new fire control system from ASELSAN by 2010.

Between 1983 and 1984, Krauss-Maffei once again turned on the production lines to build factory-fresh Leopard 1 tanks, producing 106 A3s with some modifications for **Greece** (as Leopard 1 GR1). In 1992, the Netherlands handed over a total of 168 of its upgraded tanks (1-V variant) to Athens, followed by contracts for a further 245 Leopard 1 A5s from Bundeswehr stocks (as Leopard 1 GR2) until 1998. In 2001 it was decided to upgrade 225 Leos to the A5 variant; the remaining vehicles were to be converted to special tanks. In 2005 Athens procured another 150 Leopard 1 A5s. The Leopard 1 main battle tank is still in service with the Greek Army.

In 1997 **Brazil** bought 87 Leopard 1 BEs from Belgium. The Exército Brasileiro (Brazilian Army) lists them as Leopard 1 A1. Later the deal was extended by 41 more tanks. Between 2009 and 2011, Brazil received another 220 Leopard 1 A5 from Germany.

In 1998, **Chile** agreed with the Netherlands to purchase 202 Leopard 1-Vs, which had previously been equipped with the PZB 200 passive targeting and observation system. Chile continues the Dutch designation.

At the end of the 2000s, Chile sold 30 Dutch Leopard 1-Vs to **Ecuador**.

References for this Chapter

Surprise, surprise, once again, Rolf Hilmes' Leopard 1 guide (2011) is, of course, the standard reference for comprehensive information on Leopard 1. Interestingly, Hilmes speaks of a total of 2,437 tanks handed over to the German Army. But if you add up the numbers of all produced units (also at Hilmes), you only get 2.421 Leopard 1s. Presumably, the discrepancy is due to prototypes or other special tanks assigned to the main battle tank category. Other vehicles on Leo 1 platforms, such as recovery tanks, have definitely not been included. For more information on the Leo 1, see Army Guide and Army Vehicles (both undated). That the Leopard 1 is a successful product can be observed on Krauss-Maffei Wegmann's website (undated, a). The Stoltenberg case is laid out in an article in the Spiegel (1992). For the sale of Leopard 1s to Ecuador, I fell back on Bromley & Guevara's publication (2014). I took additional information about the Danish Leos from Frank Lobitz (2009). Concerning the Norwegian Leopard 1, he speaks of 59 Leopard 1 A1A2s – I guess this is a mistake; what he means is the Leopard 1 A1A1. An overview of German tank deliveries can be found at the Bundeszentrale für politische Bildung (2012). That the Italian Army no longer uses the Leopard 1 can be proven by the Italian Ministry of Defence website: Esercito (2019). The Canadian Armed Forces have also dismissed the Leopard 1, as Scott Franklin reports (2018). Also, compare Kurschinski, K. (2014), and Schulze (2010b) for the Canadian C2 variant. The preparations for the Kosovo mission can be traced in Maloney (2019). Hodge (2004) may be of use for the delivery of Leopard 1 to Turkey. For the modernization of the Turkish Leopard 1 fleet, see Defence Turkey (2010). Global Security (undated) gives insights into the current situation of the Turkish Leos. For Greece, see Greek Military Photos (undated). Also, note about Greece: In his 2009 publication, Frank Lobitz talks about the procurement of 150 Leopard 1s in 2005. Neither Rolf Hilmes nor UNROCA (undated) refers to such a purchase – the UN arms register is incomplete, however, as it does not reveal the deal with the Netherlands, for example, and possibly does not differentiate between main battle tanks and special tanks, which would at least explain the often slightly upwardly deviating figures for Leopard ex- and imports. Nonetheless, the acquisition of 150 Leopard 1 A5s by Greece can be comprehended by the German government's answer to a Kleine Anfrage (= inquiry by parliamentary groups in the Bundestag) from 2013 (Bundesregierung, 2013). For Leopards in the service of Denmark, see Sørensen (2020) additionally. Norway's phasing out of the Leopard 1 can be traced in Harald Jacobsen's article (2011). The Australian Department of Defence's unusual offer to private individuals can be read about in Ian McPhedran (2007). Smit's 2014 publication deals with the Dutch Leopard 1, while Strategy Page (2009) provides information on Leopard tanks in South America. Verboven (2014) reports on the decommissioning of Belgian Leopards.

Combat History

Turkish Leopards against the PKK

Carl Hodges reports on Leopard 1 tanks' deployment against militant Kurds on Turkish territory in the early 1990s. Furthermore, in 1994 Turkish military officials had confirmed to a visiting group of the Bremen Senate around the Ausländerbeauftragte (= commissioner for foreigners) Dagmar Lill (SPD; Social Democratic Party of Germany), that they would use the Leopard 1 in the fight against the PKK. Medico International found out that Turkey was using its Leopard tanks (the Leos are explicitly mentioned in the report) to expel Kurdish parts of the population, allegedly committing numerous human rights violations.

It is impossible to reconstruct from the available sources, in which explicit operations Leopard 1 tanks were used. The Turkish side is very reticent about freely accessible information – possibly with good reason. The journalist Aliza Marcus, a renowned expert on the conflict between Turkey and the Kurds, mentions in her book "Blood and Belief: The PKK and the Kurdish Fight for Independence" at six points Turkish main battle tanks, without specifying the tank types used. For the sake of completeness, I will treat these mentions in the following without being able to confirm whether Leopard 1 tanks were used and, if so, in which operations:

According to Marcus, in the spring of 1990, the Turkish military sent battle tanks to Nusaybin on the Syrian border, among other places, where the mood had changed to violence against the security authorities after the funeral of a Kurdish fighter. Defense measures against tanks also occasionally played a role in Kurdish fighters' considerations, such as setting up roadblocks. This is further proof that Turkish main battle tanks were a constant factor in the confrontation with Kurdish fighters. In the late summer of 1993 (presumably August or September), a Turkish tank brigade opened up on the city center in Cizre on the Syrian border after suspected PKK fighters had fired shots. The tank fire killed an elderly man and two children, and four people were injured. In the summer of 1995, Turkish tank fire stopped a trek of Kurdish fighters trying to cross the border into Iraq.

Leo 1 in Bosnia and Croatia

After the Danish Armed Forces had already sent around 1,400 soldiers to the Balkans within UNPROFOR's mandate, the UN requested Copenhagen to provide additional troops to strengthen the security situation in Tuzla in the north of today's Bosnia and Herzegovina. For this additional contingent, the Hæren – the Royal Danish Army – also planned on augmenting it with Leopard 1 A5 DK main battle tanks. After an inner-Danish debate, which revolved around the question of whether the deployment of battle tanks was an act of warmongering, the commander of the Danish Armed Forces, General Jørgen Lyng, was able to make the deployment of Leopards acceptable to the Danish parliament with the following argument: The tanks would finally be painted white as part of the UN mission, which would reduce their martial appearance. In fact, Danish Leopard tanks appeared in the UNPROFOR mission exclusively in white, which led to the nickname "Snow Leopards." On August 17, 1993, the Danish parliament approved the deployment with a planned start of the engagement from October of the same year as part of the Nordic Battalion in Tuzla. This additional contingent's mission was to ensure the internal security of the assigned area of responsibility and provide humanitarian aid to the population. To this end, absolute freedom of movement was to be enforced throughout the entire area of responsibility;

convoys of aid supplies were to be escorted, and the general situation was to be stabilized. Tuzla should be established as a safe haven in Bosnia.

The interim period until the start of the mission was used for pre-deployment training with a Danish-Swedish exercise as the highlight. The first contingent consisted of volunteers from the Jydske Dragonregiment, composed of a staff Deling, a tank Deling from 1st Company of 3rd Panserbataljon, a tank Deling from 1st and 2nd Company of 2nd Panserbataljon, and a reinforced maintenance and supply Deling, which together formed an Eskadron for the mission.

Note: In Germany, a tank troop is an unknown formation. The Danish military formally uses the Deling (= troop) as the smallest organizational tank unit, consisting of three tanks and one off-road vehicle (this is to be replaced by an M113 transport tank on abroad operations). The Delingsfører (commander of the troop) leads the first tank, the Delingssergent (first non-commissioned officer of the troop) the second one. In the Anglo-Saxon linguistic area, this formation size is commonly called troop or troup. Consequently, tank troops exist, among others in the Canadian army. The German equivalent of the Deling or tank troop would probably be the Panzerzug. The Eskadron is the Danish equivalent of the German tank company; the Canadians use the term squadron. A Kandak is the Afghan equivalent of a battalion.

The 1st rotation of the Bosnia squadron was designated Danish Squadron, Team 1 (DANSQN 1), commanded by Kim Madsen. During UNPROFOR, IFOR, and SFOR, one Leopard of the squadron was usually equipped with a dozer blade and another with a mine plow – although these expansion kits were only mounted when necessary, as they affect the driving characteristics. In 1993, the Hæren was in the midst of converting its tank fleet to the Leopard 1 A5 DK variant. Therefore, the material situation was tricky, so the Federal Republic of Germany quickly had 20 of its Leopard 1s dismantled to supply the Danes with their turrets.

In a press conference on September 14, 1993, the Leopard tanks' mission in Bosnia was outlined. These were to be used as armored, mobile observation posts for reconnaissance purposes day and night in all weather conditions. Show of force patrols, recovery of disabled UN vehicles, and clearing of mines utilizing mine plows were also envisaged. The tanks were also meant to protect the lives of Danish soldiers.

The Leos and their crews were taken by train to Pančevo in Serbia in mid-October, where for the Danes, an agonizing period of months of waiting began. What had happened? Well, Belgrade was not particularly happy about the prospect of UN main battle tanks in Bosnia and Herzegovina and therefore put numerous bureaucratic obstacles in the way of the Danes. At the same time, a political tug of war was taking place within the United Nations. Both of these led to the Danes first being stranded in Pančevo.

On 17 January 1994, the journey could be continued over large detours: By train, the Danish troops went to Trieste and from there by a British navy ship on to Split in Croatia, where it came to an unexpected stop of about a month because an open dispute had broken out among UNPROFOR decision-makers over whether main battle tanks on the territory of Bosnia would bring new opportunities or new levels of escalation.

Only the order by the commander of the UN troops in Bosnia, General Michael Rose (Great Britain), in mid-February put an end to this episode of waiting. He ordered the Leopard tanks to move to Tuzla as a tactical reserve, which caused some trouble within the UN. First by truck and later on tracks, the Danish Leos marched to Tuzla, where they arrived about five months late to the original plan. The march was arduous because the weather was icy, and the driving conditions were terrible. The Leopard tanks waded through several bodies of water, as dilapidated bridges could not be used.

On-site, the Danes were accommodated in Camp Gønge. Meanwhile, 1st Eskadron of 1st Panserbataljon/Jydske Dragonregiment underwent operational training before taking over in Tuzla as DANSQN 2 in March 1994. The training already included experiences from the first rotation. For example, delays during transport through barricades were simulated. Therefore, the

Leopard tanks of DANSQN1 did not experience any combat situations before their successors took over.

DANSQN 2 took on the role of a quick reaction force in addition to the tasks already described. Whenever UN observation posts in the area of responsibility came under artillery fire, the Leopards could be called upon to conduct a show of force operation. The Danish tankers always worked together with a Forward Air Control Team for air support.

In the Danes' area of responsibility, periodic artillery strikes against those UN observation posts by Bosnian Serb troops posed a significant problem. The narrowly defined rules of engagement, which gave the peacekeepers little room for military reactions, made it almost impossible to respond to such attacks. The blue helmets felt abandoned, which increasingly affected their morale. Therefore, the commander of the Nordic Battalion saw the appearance of the Danish tanks in combination with the Forward Air Controllers as an instrument to stop the artillery attacks.

On April 4, 1994, Danish Leopards fired their first live ammunition in Bosnia within a combat situation. The incident took place at Gradačac 70 kilometers north of Tuzla, where a Leo Deling, a Forward Air Control Team, and a Swedish armored personnel carrier as part of a patrol secured a convoy carrying humanitarian aid supplies. At 13:20 hrs, a machine gun or autocannon opened fire on the tank of the Delingssergent. Shortly afterward, the tank of the Delingsfører also came under fire. In both cases, the enemy gunner missed his target. The Danes first retreated and met their Eskadron commander, Major Carsten Rasmussen. He ordered them to resume patrolling. At 14:33 hrs, the Leos again reached the scene of the incident and once again came under fire. After the Danes had fogged themselves by using their smoke mortars and changed positions under the smoke, the Delingsfører identified a 40-millimeter gun at a distance of 2,340 meters. His tank destroyed the target with two High-Explosive rounds. The Danes then left the scene of the incident when two artillery rounds hit. The splinter effects scratched the paint job of one Leo.

On April 29, 1994, a second incident went down in the annals of Leopard history as Operation Bøllebank. Bøllebank was a contingency plan for the deployment of Danish tanks in case of an attack by the army of the Republika Srpska or the Yugoslav People's Army. On that April 29th, the Swedish observation post, code name Tango 2, which was manned by seven soldiers, near Kalesija was first fired upon by the Zvornik Brigade at 21:40 hrs with high angle fire and rockets, then again at 22:00 hrs – it was the 28th attack on Tango 2! After previous NATO airstrikes and the hostage-taking of UN soldiers by Bosnian Serbs, the overall situation was also considered extremely tense.

The commander of the Nordic Battalion then ordered two Danish tank troops (1st Deling under the command of Claus Andresen and 2nd Deling under Erik Kirk, plus Major Rasmussen with his tank, which added up to seven Leos) and a Swedish armored personnel carrier to Saraci to make contact with the forward command post, where deputy battalion commander Oberst Lars Møller, who himself had an armored personnel carrier at his disposal, was present at the time. The Leopards hurried to their destination at top speed and with all lights switched on to scare the attackers away.

During a briefing in Saraci, three artillery rounds hit in the immediate vicinity of the UN soldiers at around 23:15 hrs. Thereupon the two tank troops swarmed out. The 2nd Deling took fire positions in the southern part of Saraci. The 1st Deling, together with Rasmussen and Møller, rushed to Kalesija and again came under massive fire on the march so that the tankers switched off the lights. For 15 to 20 minutes, they were fired upon by forces of the Sekovici Brigade. No sooner had they arrived in Kalesija than Bosnian Serbs from camouflaged positions and apparently equipped with night-vision devices opened fire on the UN tanks. A first anti-tank missile detonated between the two Leopards who had taken the rearmost positions in the column. Immediately afterward, another anti-tank missile hit a factory, in whose protection Møller's personnel carrier was parked, so that debris rained down on it. A third anti-tank missile dashed directly toward the last Leopard of the column. The driver recognized the danger and stepped on the brakes so that the missile in front of his tank ripped open the road. A fourth anti-tank missile also hit the vicinity while muzzle flashes of automatic weapons flashed in the dark in the distance. The Danes asked for air support, which was refused. Møller, Rasmussen, and the rearmost Leopard of the column hold the ground, the remaining tanks of the troop tried to break through to Tango 2. Møller and Co. sought shelter between the buildings, while heavy artillery fire rained down on Kalesija. It is not clear if Møller or Rasmussen gave the initial order to fire, but the Danish Leo's of the 1st Deling eventually started to defend themselves at 11:45 hrs. Also, from Saraci, the 2nd Deling opened fire on identified enemy positions. The fighting partly took place at distances of up to 4,200 meters. Several bunkers, from which anti-tank missiles had been fired, were destroyed, but at the same time, the forces of the Sekovici Brigade opened fire on the Danes from ever new positions. The UN soldiers in Kalesija advanced to the western part of the village, and from 00:05 hrs, they concentrated their fire on positions on Mount Vis, from the top of which, among other things, a 100-millimeters anti-tank gun T-12 shot at them. Next to it, there was a bunker from which the enemy fire seemed to be coordinated. The engagement range was 4,140 meters. After both targets had been eliminated, the Bosnian Serb troops ceased fire for about 30 minutes. Simultaneously with the shelling of Mount Vis, the two remaining tanks of the 1st Deling finally broke through to Tango 2 and from there took further enemy emplacements under fire.

After a brief situation report, the forces around Møller left town in the direction of Saraci. Hardly on the march were they again caught in intense enemy fire from mountain Vis. Møller gave the 2nd Deling the order to fire once more at 00:40 hrs, at which point they fought for 15 to 20 minutes against the enemy. The 2nd tank of 2nd Deling fired one last round, which caused a giant explosion on the other side – an ammunition depot was hit and blew up. The UN forces surrounding Møller reached Saraci without losses. The enemy fire died away, and the Danes withdrew to Camp Gønge after 01:00 hrs, except for the two Leopard tanks at Tango 2, which stayed on the spot for several days. The firing positions of the 2nd Deling were covered with artillery fire again after the tanks had withdrawn.

During the two-hour action, the Danes fired a total of 44 HE round, nine phosphorus rounds, and 19 armor-piercing shells. The Bosnian Serbs reported nine dead, but other reports assume up to 150 dead and as many wounded. The Danes suffered no losses, although one Leo received a direct hit. A splinter slightly wounded Møller.

Consequently, the United Nations imposed strict restrictions on the further activity of DANSQN to avoid further escalation. The UN feared being drawn into the military conflict. The incident was also widely reported in the Danish press, according to Sørensen, in a mostly positive manner. In 1998 Kirk and Møller were awarded the Ebbe Muncks Prize of Honour for their accomplishment of Operation Bøllebank.

During the hot summer months, the immense heat production of the Leopard's mechanical components combined with the lack of air conditioning had adverse effects on the tanks and tankers.

In October 1994, DANSQN 3 took over. The tankmen were recruited from soldiers of the Dronningens Livregiment and the Prinsens Livregiment. The range of tasks of the Danish Leopard detachment was extended by so-called "social patrols" – patrol operations in the area of responsibility on which the population was helped with concrete problems. At the same time, freedom of movement was ensured, and the surrounding area could be observed.

As early as October 26, 1994, Operation Amanda was the next incident that led to shots being fired in anger. Previously Bosnian Serb soldiers had denied a Swedish company to enter observation post S01 near the Bøllebank battlefield. Between October 19 and 24, several attempts were made to man the observation post, each time thwarted by incoming fire. The 1st Deling of the Danish Leos was given the task of investigating the site if the observation post had to be evacuated or reinforced. Together with the Swedes, the Danish tanks moved out. On-site, an explosive round detonated only 50 meters from the tank of the troop leader. The UN forces then withdrew. Shortly afterward, the Leopards were reinforced with a medical armored personnel carrier and a recovery tank; it now consisted of three Leos, the vehicles mentioned above, and an M113 APC. One Leopard was equipped with a dozer blade. Together with other forces of the Eskadron, the Deling left the camp again at noon on October 25, 1994.

The Danish army used the Leopard 1 A5 DK under UN command in former Yugoslavia during the civil war in the 1990s. A number of these vehicles were later upgraded to the standard Leopard 1 A5 DK (SFOR) with an external generator and cooling system. This vehicle is currently in the collection of one of the Regiment Museum Associations in Denmark (Copyright Thomas Antonsen)

In the target area, the M113 was used to explore the terrain. Thus favorable firing positions for the Leos were identified, and it was decided to consolidate them under cover of darkness by the tank with a dozer blade. Said work began at 21:00 hrs.

The next morning at 08:00 hrs, the last preparations for the upcoming operation were made. The Forward Air Control Team was deployed at observation post S02. The Leo's gunners loaded the main armament with an armor-piercing round.

At 13:35 hrs, the area around S02 was fired upon for the first time. At 14:46 hrs, the order was given to the tank troop to take up the prepared firing positions at S01. On the spot, an artillery shell detonated only 20 meters in front of the vehicle of the Delingsfører. The commander of the Eskadron gave permission to open fire on visible targets. His tank then shot at a dam at a distance of 5,100 meters, where an enemy gun was suspected. Afterward, the squadron commander's tank changed position when the enemy opened fire again. One HE round hit a house about 20 meters away from the Leopard tank. Its crew responded with a High-Explosive shell themselves, after which a smoke shell struck their Leo head-on. The hit destroyed the left towing hook, damaged the headlight, and painted parts of the hull yellow-orange. None of the crew members were wounded. At the same time, it was announced that air support was expected in 20 minutes.

The tank of the Delingssergent fired four rounds at presumable emplacements of Bosnian Serbs within minutes. At this time, the Danes reconnoitered an enemy tank at a distance of 4,100 meters. The thermal image showed that the main gun's barrel was cold, so the tank had not fired yet. Instead, the Danes exchanged bullets with other Bosnian Serb positions for some time, with the enemy also shelling the UN soldiers with artillery. Then a muzzle flash was spotted at 5,100 meters and thus yet another T-55 main battle tank. The Danish Leopards responded with several shots against that tank. More indirect fire reached the UN soldiers, who marked the Leos' fire positions with smoke as the requested fighter planes approached. However, the fighter planes did not attack, so the men and women of DANSQN eventually withdrew.

The Danish Leopards had fired a total of 21 rounds during this encounter. The reasons for the withdrawal were the UN ban on using ground forces to counter enemy artillery fire and the threat posed to Tuzla by Bosnian Serb artillery fire. The Bosnia and Herzegovina Armed Forces subsequently claimed to have learned that Republika Srpska had lost a 76-millimeter mountain gun M-48B1 in the fight. The T-55 was considered damaged and thus temporarily inoperable.

DANSQN 3 was followed by DANSQN 4 in March 1995 and finally DANSQN 5 from October 1995 onwards, without the Leopards being involved in any further combat operations.

On the night of December 19-20, 1995, NATO took over responsibility; UNPROFOR became IFOR. The Danish tanks' white UN-paint job was provisionally transformed overnight with green and black paint into a camouflage pattern. On the morning of December 20, the tank Eskadron began its first mission: It advanced into the Posavina corridor to test whether the appearance under NATO mandate changed anything. During this operation, U.S. units mistook the Danes for troops of the Bosnian Serbs. Since all sides kept a cool head, the confusion did not end in disaster.

On January 13, 1996, the Leopards finally received the Danish tank force's standard paint job.

During the IFOR mission, the Danish tanks were not involved in any combat. However, an incident occurred in connection with anti-tank mines: at the end of January 1996, a patrol of Leos reached a checkpoint west of Doboj. The road was covered with snow, so it was not possible to see what was underneath. During a turning maneuver, the tank of the Delingssergent, equipped with the mine plow, hit a TMM-1 mine loaded with a whopping 5.6 kilograms of explosives. The detonation set off a chain reaction in which three more mines lurking under the snow cover blew up – one detonated about half a meter away from the tank, one directly under the first and second road wheel on the right and left sides, and one under the tank at the level of the fire control computer. Fortunately, the Leo's armor withstood, but the commander was wounded by shrapnel. The rest of the crew was shaken harshly (it can be assumed that they were at least slightly wounded, for example, suffering a whiplash). Also, several cartridges for both the main armament and secondary weapon fell out of their mounts; one High-Explosive round was dented; overall several were damaged.

The tank was heavily damaged. The blast lifted the turret by about 10 centimeters on one side. The electronics in the turret failed, and the fire control computer was severely damaged. The entire hull suffered damage due to splintering effects. The armor on the underbody was torn open. Road wheels and tracks were partially destroyed.

However, the Leopard's engine was still running when the noise of the explosion subsided. The vehicle was later returned to Denmark, and the hull was replaced with a replacement hull from Germany before the tank (thus the only Danish vehicle with old-style exhaust grilles) was used again in the Balkans. This Leo is still kept in running condition by the Danish Army.

The Danish tank force supported the IFOR mission with three rotations; the change of rotations took place in March/April 1996 and October 1996. During the second rotation deployment, the tanks were retrofitted with air conditioning and power generators (and thus upgraded to the Leopard 1 A5 DK-1 variant).

In December 1996, SFOR superseded IFOR, which for the Danish Leopards meant an expansion of its rules of engagement and range of tasks. A new task was to enable refugees to return to their homeland. The Danish contingent was reduced in personnel. Due to the positive development of the overall situation, military training of the deployed troops in Bosnia was expanded. Besides, more international joint exercises were conducted in the area of operation. In December 2002, the Danish contingent was reduced once again. The Leo Eskadron was transferred to Tuzla and placed under the Multinational Brigade's (USA) command. In August

2003, the Leopards were ordered back home after almost ten years of service in Bosnia. The return journey was made by train and ship. Since the transition to SFOR, a total of 15 rotations had been deployed. There were no incidents involving the use of arms; the recovery of stuck vehicles was still one of the most extraordinary tasks for the Danish tankers.

Also, Belgium's Leopard force should find mention at this point. According to the Belgian Armed Forces website, Brussels deployed the Leopard 1 "in the former Yugoslavia" (Verboven, S., 2014, translation via Google Translator), which is rather unspecific. The French Wikipedia article on the Gidsen regiment (former Belgian tank unit equipped with the Leopard 1) speaks more specifically of an engagement in Croatia in the early 1990s, unfortunately without any sources given. Therefore, it remains unclear to what extent and with what mission Belgian Leopards were sent on missions in Croatia, Bosnia, and Herzegovina, and what their crews experienced there. The lack of information allows the conclusion that Belgian Leopards were not involved in any significant combat operations.

Leopards in Kosovo

Denmark also used tanks Leopard 1 A5 DK-1 and Canada Leopard 1 C1 within the KFOR mission framework in Kosovo. This means that small Denmark even provided tank troops for two NATO missions at the same time.

Canadian Leopards were initially planned for Operation Cobra as part of Determined Effort in the strength of a squadron, to be able to extract UN troops on the territory of the former Yugoslavia with a powerful task force in the event of an emergency. However, this operation was never carried out. Later, the Canadians participated in the invasion of Kosovo from Macedonia with about 800 soldiers; the Canadian KFOR contingent operated under the name Operation Kinetic.

On April 1, 1999, the Deputy Chief of the Defence Staff, Lieutenant-General Ray Henault, gave his planners the order to prepare a battle group in the context of a possible ground-based KFOR operation led by NATO. The structure of the battle group was presented to the cabinet on June 1. As part of it, 19 Leopard 1 C1s were considered, combined into a squadron. However, the cabinet initially prohibited the use of tanks for cost reasons. According to Sean Maloney, the branding of main battle tanks as weapons of a war of aggression, which had been developed during the Trudeau administration in the 1970s and has been stuck in Canadian politicians' minds ever since, also played an important role. On the other hand, the Canadian government needed to make a visible and noticeable contribution to NATO's engagement in Kosovo to emphasize its own importance as a military ally and secure influence on the future development. Between these priorities, the deployment of 19 Leopard tanks as part of the original Kinetic force with a total of around 550 vehicles was the subject of very controversial discussions from the beginning of June. In the end, the compromise provided for a significantly reduced combat force: a battalion consisting of two infantry companies and one tank troop. In addition to other units, a pioneer squadron, as well as a staff and a supply element (National Command Element and National Support Element), served as support.

A further challenge was the transfer of the troops to the Balkans. Since the 1990s, the Canadian military has massively reduced its logistical potential, making it dependent on the help of third parties for the shipment of troops. When a member of the logistics staff finally stated that a transfer to the Balkans would hardly be thinkable before November 2001, panic broke out. Canada did not want to keep its reputation as a nation that joined military operations only after any danger had largely been eliminated.

The Lord Strathcona's Horse (Royal Canadians) was selected to provide tanks and personnel for the first rotation. In the Balkans, the Canadian tankers would operate under the umbrella of the British Armed Forces' 4th Armoured Brigade, led by Brigadier Bill Rollo. The British brigade was meant to form the Multinational Brigade Center (MNB (C)). Initially, Lieutenant-Colonel Steven Bryan commanded the battle group. He was replaced by Lieutenant-Colonel Shane Brennan in the course of the rotation.

A first twelve-man contingent of a company of the mechanized reconnaissance squadron of the Strathcona's under Major Paul Fleury's command arrived in Macedonia in May 1999. The large equipment of the Canadian battle group was to be embarked via Thessaloniki. The Canadians gathered the same negative experience in the Greek port city as many other NATO partners. Violent demonstrators posed a severe problem in and around Thessaloniki, and the Greek authorities often showed little cooperation. The Canadian soldiers found themselves in a thoroughly hostile atmosphere as soon as they set foot on European soil.

On June 7, 1999, the 4th Armoured Brigade issued the warning order to invade Kosovo, which was called Operation Agricola. It was still unclear which Canadian forces would be available to the brigade and when. Substantial parts of the planned battle group were still not in the Balkans, so the invasion of Kosovo finally took place without Canadian Leopards.

They arrived between July 24 and August 4, 1999, in the strength of five Leopard 1 C1s, thus completing the Canadian battle group. (Maloney's book, which features many contemporary witnesses, occasionally contradicts itself about the numbers – for example, there is sometimes talk of only four Leopards for KFOR). MEXAS composite armor elements had been mounted shortly before shipment.

A Canadian NCO remarks in Maloney's book, not without irony that the Canadian armed forces have once again opted for the cheapest possible transport option. In fact, the soldiers had flown from Canada to Skopje in old rattletrap planes, almost without food, and no one had been allowed to leave the plane during the stopovers. And the large equipment had been shipped to Greece on a Ukrainian cargo ship. On arrival, the tank soldiers and infantrymen were horrified to discover that the ship's crew had used the journey time to pick the locks and "take a look around" in the vehicles. Numerous tools and even weapons had disappeared without a trace, but the Canadians found their vehicles littered.

The Leopards were loaded onto British trucks in Thessaloniki and were finally taken to Macedonia in a mad, disorientated trip. Most of the Canadian soldiers mentioned in Sean Maloney's book describe the march as one of chaos and torture. Numerous hand weapons of the Canadian army were shipped to Europe without the corresponding firing pins – these had been forgotten in Canada so that some convoys had to make the overland journey to Macedonia almost unarmed.

The Strathcona's sent a tank advisor to the battle group headquarters (Captain Don Senft in the first rotation). Brigadier Rollo set Drenica as the Canadians' area of responsibility, a hilly and mine-infested region northwest of Pristina. The UÇK had several strongpoints in Drenica, and the crucial east-west road (Route Dog) ran through this region. Therefore, Rollo needed a relatively autonomous, mobile, force that was able to earn respect by showing off impressive military equipment to secure Drenica. The Canadians were able to offer both with their LAV II armored vehicles, their APCs, and last but not least, with their Leopard 1 C1 main battle tanks. Besides Drecina, the battle group was assigned the areas north and south of the airport of Pristina. The battle group was able to report readiness for duty in its area of responsibility by August 1999.

In the event of an attack of Belgrade's Armed Forces on Kosovo, the Canadian battle group was designated for pushing with its mechanized troops into the area around Podujeva north of Pristina, where it was to counterattack and destroy attacking enemy forces. The Canadian Leopards were to be deployed on the left flank of the MNB (C), i.e., on the road from Mitrovica to Pristina. In this scenario, they were to be supported by a British squadron of the MNB (C), equipped with Challenger tanks, and by the German Leopard 2 A5 of the MNB (South).

In addition to being involved in emergency planning for a possible war with Serbia, the Canadian Leopards conducted operations where illegal police stations and the like were closed down. They were also involved in running checkpoints. The Canadians made a point of carrying out such operations in a visible manner to demonstrate strength. Battle tanks were a tried and tested means for this. According to Operations Officer Major Jerry Walsh, the Leos significantly increased the Canadian's political weight within KFOR, even though the Army had requested a squadron and ended up with only a handful of tanks. In a quote from Sean Maloney's book, Don Senft emphasizes the tanks' psychological effect on potential attackers. He sees particular advantages in the Leopard 1 C1 because it is lighter and more agile than many other nations' main battle tanks.

For the Leopards of the Danish Hæren, the journey to Kosovo began in 1999 in Esbjerg, after the preparatory mission training had been completed. Transferring the troops was handled by the private logistics company DFDS. The Danske Livregiment provided the personnel of the first rotation. The Danish KFOR contingent also did not participate in the invasion of Kosovo. Instead, an advance staff arrived in the Balkans on July 29, 1999, and most of the Danish contingent followed until August 10. The total strength amounted to a battalion, including a tank Eskadron equipped with Leopards of type 1 A5 DK-1, stationed in Camp Olaf Rye. The Danish forces were under the Multinational Brigade North (MNB (N)), which was led by France. The Danes' AoR was an area of about 30 square kilometers west of Mitrovica to the Serbian border.

A Deling of the Eskadron was permanently stationed at the permanent border checkpoint D-31 at Gazivoda Lake. A second troop was on standby as a permanent quick reaction force (combat readiness within 30 minutes). A third Deling patrolled from the camp through the area of responsibility or set up temporary checkpoints. The three troops rotated weekly. Each was equipped in the same way as in Bosnia. In Kosovo, recovering stuck vehicles was one of the most extraordinary operations the Danish tanks conducted, including pulling a Leopard from the front yard of a villager. Another highlight was the visit of Prince Henrik, who was especially interested in the Leos.

On August 22, 1999, Brigadier Peter Pearson, commander of the 19th Mechanized Brigade, took over command of the Canadian battle group. The Canadian Leopards then were attached to B Company (Major David Corbould), which was stationed south of the airport. Therefore the tankers set up their base in Kuzmin west of Pristina, as the Serbian community there was in constant danger of attacks by Albanian guerrillas. The main roads were also easy to reach from there. Subsequently, the Strathcona's soldiers also took part in patrols on foot. Among others, B Company's area of responsibility included the village of Staro Gracko, where 14 Serbs were murdered in July 1999.

The Leopards regularly patrolled in two-tank formations criss-cross the whole AoR to be always seen by the population. The Canadians removed all identification numbers and so on from their tanks to make it difficult for observers to identify the unit. Due to the few Leopards' high activities, the men of the UÇK soon believed they were dealing with 25 to 30 Canadian tanks. The Leos were also used in ethnic unrest and to protect individuals or groups of individuals.

B Company's Area of Responsibility also bordered on the Russian sector – and soon several problems occurred with this very ally. The highlight was a clash one night between a Russian BTR-80 armored personnel carrier and a Canadian Leopard main battle tank. The crew of the BTR was drunk. The armored car raced towards some Canadians at full speed and only veered away when one Leopard, which was on-site, pointed its main gun at it. The Canadians could then watch the crew being intercepted by other Russian soldiers, dragged out of their vehicle, beaten, and taken away.

Another incident occurred in Vrelo, where a Russian BTR dashed through the town at a crazy velocity. The Canadians tried to block the armored car with their vehicles and finally succeeded in encircling it in the town center. Attempts to get the crew out of the BTR failed. Lastly, two Leopard 1s were called in. That was when the armored personnel carrier's turret with its 12.7-millimeter machine gun began to aim at Canadian targets. However, the barrel was clogged with newspapers. Corbould ordered his soldiers to retreat, which caused the driver of the BTR to step on the gas once more. Again his armored car drove through the streets of Vrelo at breakneck speed. It was only when Russian officers arrived that the BTR's tour ended. This incident lasted a total of six hours.

In November 1999, the Canadians participated in Operation Constant Resolve. NATO troops, including several Canadian Leopard tanks under the command of Lieutenant Ray Miksa, deployed near the border with Serbia to study the Yugoslav army's reaction to it. They had to repeat their deployment maneuver three times before the other side reacted: the Serbs finally brought battle tanks into position and dropped infantry by helicopter on their side of the border.

In December 1999, a new rotation took over (Operation Kinetic Roto 1), the British 7th Armoured Brigade under Brigadier Richard Shirreff assumed command over the Canadian battle group. The Leopard crews of this rotation came from the Royal Canadian Dragoons. Lieutenant-Colonel Bruce Pennington commanded the battle group. The Leos' role changed with the change of rotation; they were now less active but waited on standby for possible engagements.

Canada withdrew entirely from its military engagement in Kosovo in June 2000.

In August 2000, when the third Danish rotation replaced the second, the Danish Leos were withdrawn from Kosovo and replaced by an anti-tank platoon.

The participation of the Belgian tank force in the KFOR mission can only be fragmentarily treated due to a lack of publicly available sources: For example, the Leopard Club website, which is aimed primarily at model builders, reports that Belgian Leopard 1 A5 BEs were deployed by the Gidsen regiment in 2000 and 2001 in northern Kosovo on a strategic hill codenamed Notting Hill near Leposavić, which was in the AOR of the Multinational Brigade (North). An article in the magazine Zeitschrift für Mitglieder und Freunde des Heimat- und Geschichtsvereins Troisdorf e.V. partly supports this depiction. According to it, the Gidsen Regiment was stationed in Troisdorf, Germany, until the new millennium. From there, 2,000 Belgian soldiers were sent off to Kosovo in April – it remains unclear whether there were also tanks and tankers among them. Photos of Belgian Leopards with KFOR inscriptions can also be found on the Internet. Details of the deployment of Belgian Leos in Kosovo are unknown, but the photos suggest that the Belgian Leos were involved in running temporary checkpoints. The lack of information suggests that the Belgian tanks were not involved in combat operations.

In his publication on Operation Kinetic, Sean Maloney writes that all NATO states involved had equipped their KFOR troops with main battle tanks, or at least the Canadian cabinet assumed so in the summer of 1999. That would mean that countries such as Norway or Italy might also have sent Leopard tanks to Kosovo, but there is no evidence.

Leopards at the Hindu Kush

Canada also initially relied on the Leopard 1 in the ISAF mission. But first things first, we have to talk about offensive Operation Medusa, for which Canadian ISAF troops made use of three bulldozers enhanced with armor plates in September 2006. The operation was a significant blow against the insurgents. What was remarkable about Medusa was that the Taliban, who otherwise practiced guerrilla warfare, had established a conventional front line at Pashmul. They included poppy and grape fields, wadis, and other obstacles into this front line, occupying it with their fighters. Many emplacements were connected, forming a coherent system of partly entrenched positions up to real bunkers. Additionally the front line was secured by IEDs (improvised explosive devices) and mines. All access roads were guarded by Taliban fighters and/or secured with booby traps. The Canadian battle group was in charge of the offensive and was supported by Danish, Afghan, and Dutch forces as well as Canadian and U.S. commandos. With an attack on both banks of the Arghandāb River north and south of Pashmul, ISAF forces engaged the Taliban system of emplacements. Like 90 years earlier on the battlefields of World War I, the Canadians shelled enemy positions with artillery preparation fire before charging. Covered from ISAF air forces, they cut safe lanes into fields with their bulldozers and overcame wadis and creeks with them to finally break through the enemy's defenses. By September 13, the Taliban capitulated in Zhari and Pashmul. They suffered at least hundreds of casualties; some estimates range up to 2,000 killed insurgents. More than 100 Canadians lost their lives or were seriously wounded in the fighting, which led to a major debate back at home. Operation Medusa impaired but did not break the power base of the insurgents in Kandahar. Even after that, the region remained the scene of numerous attacks by insurgents on Afghan security authorities and foreign troops or organizations.

However, Medusa made it clear to the Canadians that main battle tanks were necessary for ISAF operations. They needed heavy tracked vehicles to overcome obstacles and barriers and more firepower than the 25-millimeter chain gun of the Canadian infantry fighting vehicle LAV III could deliver. This realization, which was conveyed to Ottawa by the commander of the 1st Battalion/The Royal Canadian Regiment, Lieutenant-Colonel Lavoie, as well as by the commander of the Regional Command South, Brigadier-General Fraser, could undoubtedly be described as precarious since the Department of National Defence had already decided to abolish its main battle tank force in 2003. At the time of Operation Medusa, the last Leopard 1s were decommissioned; instead, M1028 Stryker armored vehicles with the 105-millimeter gun were to be procured.

On September 15, 2006, Ottawa authorized the deployment of 15 Leopard 1 C2s for ISAF. This decision marks a remarkable turnaround in the strategic alignment of the Canadian military. The Lord Strathcona's Horse (Royal Canadians) was chosen to send its Leopards to Afghanistan since it was the last unit still equipped with MBTs. Lord Strathcona's Horse provided its B Squadron under Major Trevor Cadieu for the ongoing rotation.

The selected Leos were hastily equipped with additional armor packages (including new MEXAS composite armor). B Squadron was deployed on September 29, 2006. The tanks were airlifted to the country of deployment by the United States Air Force aircraft and Ukrainian AN-124 Antonov planes. It was a significant logistical achievement of the Canadian Armed Forces, bearing in mind that the deployment of a tank force is not limited to merely transporting tanks and crews. Instead, suitable personnel had to be selected and trained within a few weeks, and infrastructure for tank maintenance had to be established in Kandahar to provide supplies, spare parts, and the like. In general, the Canadian Armed Forces have been training the interaction with main battle tanks as preparation for deploying to Afghanistan since autumn 2006 as a direct response to the experience gained from Operation Medusa.

Six weeks after Ottawa agreed to the deployment of Leopards, the tanks and their crews were already in Kandahar. At the beginning of December 2006, B Squadron reported full readiness for duty, using Forward Operating Base (FOB) Ma'Sum Ghar as its base of operations. Even before full readiness for duty was achieved, Canadian Leopards took part in patrols along Route Summit. The squadrons of Lord Strathcona's Horse (Royal Canadians) A, B, and C rotated in a six-month cycle – with the first rotation of B Squadron being shorter due to the fact that this unit reinforced an ongoing rotation.

The Canadian tanks were partly equipped with mine plows and dozer blades for operations at the Hindu Kush. Since December 2006, the Leopard 1 C2 had participated in all major operations of the Canadian Armed Forces. To this end, the tank soldiers were tasked with establishing combat readiness so that they could react at any time to events in the entire area of operations of the Canadians. Leopard tanks guarded the camp from elevated positions, fired at enemy ambush positions as well as insurgents attempting to attack Canadian bases with RPGs (shoulder-fired missile weapon) or mortars. According to Major Cadieu (now Major-General), the Taliban "learned the hard way the capabilities of the Leopard's main gun" (Cadieu, T., 2008, p.7).

The first operation with Leopard participation was Canadian-led Operation Baaz Tzuka. On December 15, 2006, it started intending to drive the Taliban out of Howz-e Madad and Zangabad in the Zhari District on a lasting basis and reduce their ability to rally for a spring offensive. NATO announced the success of the operation on December 20, 2006. Leopard tanks jointly operated alongside an infantry company and an armored engineer troop in this operation.

On December 21, 2006, a company size task force consisting of Leopards and LAVs moved from Ma'Sum Ghar via Route Fenway to Mushan to secure a landing zone for Dutch infantry east of the city. They received the Dutch on December 22, who then secured Mushan and held a meeting (a so-called shura) with the village elders.

In January and February 2007, the Canadians, together with the ANA, significantly expanded their reach in a series of offensive operations. Canadian Leos broke through enemy positions, cordoned off areas, and participated in search operations. Finally, they succeeded in securing the Siah Choy area. Afterward, B Squadron, together with U.S. special forces and Canadian recce troops, was able to take full possession of the peninsula at the intersection of the Dowrey and Arghandāb rivers, putting further pressure on the enemy. It is the peninsula on which the city of Mushan is located.

In mid-February, the regular rotation change took place, but A Squadron under Major Dave Broomfield's command did not take over responsibility for the Leopards until early March.

Previously, Cadieu's Leopards of B Squadron, in joint forces with Canadian mechanized infantry of the new rotation (Hotel Company of 2nd Battalion/The Royal Canadian Regiment under Major Alex Ruff), patrolled the entire Panjwai-Zhari region incessantly, with pioneers always accompanying them to protect them from unpleasant surprises.

For almost a month, B Squadron stayed in the area of operations, participated in spoiling attacks against Taliban activities in the Kandahar-Helmand border area, and provided fire support for Afghan security authorities in Howz-e-Madad and Sangsar. Other forces always accompanied the Leopards. Typically, two tank troops of four tanks each plus the squadron staff formed one combat unit to reinforce one or more infantry companies, while another tank troop was deployed elsewhere in the AO. Leading such a joint unit of tanks and infantry was handled as follows: During attacks and breakthrough attempts, the highest-ranked officer of the Leopards commanded the entire force; during subsequent securing and consolidation phases, the senior infantry officer took over command. The Canadians often divided their forces into two formations as they advanced, each led by a Leopard with a dozer blade or mine plows. The problem with these pre-stressed expansions is that they restrain the tanks' motion behavior. Furthermore, remotely triggered IEDs, in particular, are not necessarily detonated by such equipment.

Operations in Howz-e-Madad in the Maywand district began on 23 February 2007. Cadieu's Leopards, along with two Canadian infantry companies and ANA forces, advanced along Highway 1 into an area that ISAF troops had never entered before. The target was said Howz-e-Madad, where a suspected weapons and explosives depot was to be located and seized. The insurgents were also to be made aware that ISAF and the Afghan security authorities enjoyed freedom of movement throughout Kandahar Province.

In the target area, Canadian forces surrounded the buildings in the middle of Howz-e-Madad, where the depot was suspected before the Afghans began their search. They found plenty of bombs and missiles. When they began loading their findings, the Taliban struck from all directions with small arms and RPG weapons. Civilians rushed off in confusion while Canadians and Afghans took up the firefight. The skirmish lasted only a few minutes, and the Canadians and Afghans used only small-caliber weapons. Thus te Leo's main armaments did not speak in this incident. Eventually, the attackers could be put to flight. Neither did the Afghans nor the Canadians or the Civilians suffer any casualties.

In Cadieu's report, he describes the effectiveness of Leopard operations in Afghanistan. Admittedly dividing the scarce tanks to reinforce several infantry companies simultaneously and the enormous heat (more on the climate issue below), which at times literally boiled Kandahar Province, reduced the overall effectiveness of the Canadian Leopards. Nevertheless, the tanks gave the infantry a power that, according to Cadieu, made an impression as far west as the Helmand border and north in Ghorak and Shah Wali Kot.

After the ambush in Howz-e-Madad, Broomfield and his tankers took over. The supply echelon was commanded in the new rotation by Master Warrant Officer Bill Crabb. The personnel were transported partly by civil airlines and partly by Canadian military aircraft first to the Middle East, from where they continued their journey to Afghanistan in C-130 Hercules. Forward Operating Base Ma'Sum Ghar north of Pashmul continued to serve as the base of operations.

Between early March and late May 2007, Canadian Leopard 1 C2s participated in NATO-led Operation Achilles to drive the Taliban from the northern Kandahar districts (Panjwai, Zhari, Maywand). It was a large-scale NATO spring offensive in southern Afghanistan that started on March 3, 2007. 4,500 ISAF soldiers from the USA, the Netherlands, Canada, Great Britain, and 1,000 members of the Afghan security authorities advanced against Taliban positions in the Sangin, Kajaki, Musa Kala Nasak districts. With this largest joint military operation since the fall of the Taliban government, NATO wanted to improve the security situation and pre-empt a spring offensive announced by the Taliban. One strategically important target was the dam in Kajaki, which supplies the surrounding population with drinking water. The area of operations is characterized by craggy mountains that served as retreats for the Taliban due to NATO's absolute air superiority. Besides, this was where they planned and carried out their operations. NATO was able to gain a foothold in the area of operations until the end of May but was unable to ultimately drive out the Taliban.

At the end of March, as part of the Achilles offensive, Hotel Company and A Squadron, together with Canadian pioneers under the overall command of Major Ruff, advanced west into the Maywand region to secure convoys between Kandahar and the Helmand Task Force. Ruff also held meetings with village elders in various villages to initiate infrastructure projects. With the ANP, temporary checkpoints were operated, with corruption within the Afghan police force proving to be a major shortcoming. Ruff's combat team was out in the open for more than five weeks, setting up a harbor at a different location every night. Most of the time, the enemy avoided open fighting. The insurgents occasionally fired 107-millimeter missiles at Ruff's unit, especially when they had formed a stronghold. Since the gunners seemed to be poorly trained, all but each missed its target by far. It was nevertheless remarkable that ISAF troops were able to move freely in the Panjwai and Zhari districts, which had been considered strongholds of the Taliban and the drug trade before the battle for Pashmul. Among other things, Ruff's combat team was called in to help when U.S. or British convoys became immobilized after they hit a mine or were struck by an IED. One such assignment led Broomfield's tanks to a convoy of the U.S. 82nd Airborne Division, which had lost six Humvees in a mine and IED field. Two of the Canadian tanks used mine plows to clear safe lanes to the vehicles that had been hit to enable their recovery.

On 8 April 2007, after 36 days outside in the open, interrupted only by a few short visits of ISAF bases, and shortly before the end of Operation Achilles, Ruff's combat team was to escort an ISAF convoy through the desert of Maywand to the Helmand border as the last task before proceeding to Kandahar Airfield. A platoon of Canadian Hotel Company was struck by an IED assembled from several anti-tank mines shortly after the order was given at an intersection. Six soldiers were killed, and one vehicle was heavily damaged. Broomfield's tanks did not participate in the subsequent rescue operation, but the original escort mission was canceled. Later that day, the Canadian Leopards reached Kandahar Airfield. Thus Operation Achilles ended.

During Achilles, the Canadian main battle tanks stood out for their ability to operate autonomously from forward operating bases over long distances. Special mention should be made of using the mine plows, which proved themselves very helpful in recovering vehicles and crews from old Soviet minefields.

Even after Operation Achilles, NATO sends out patrols in the Maywand region, intending to challenge the Taliban to not concentrate on spoiling reconstruction efforts. Securing important meetings with local decision-makers was also part of the Canadian ISAF forces' daily bread and, consequently, Broomfield's tanks.

On April 11, 2007, a LAV II Coyote of the Canadian recce troops was blown up by an IED near Ghundey Ghar, near the place where shortly before the soldiers of Hotel Company were struck by an IED. One man got wounded. A much more powerful second IED then blew up another Coyote of those troops hurrying to the scene. The explosion threw the vehicle into the air. One occupant was killed instantly, and another died a little later, trapped in the driver's cab. It was getting dark, and more rescue forces rushed in as indications accumulated that around 100 Taliban fighters, bomb-makers, and Chechen mercenaries had infiltrated the region. Under the impression of these reports and the ongoing evacuation and evidence collection work at the double IED attack site, the commander of the Canadian battle group, Lieutenant-Colonel Rob Walker, ordered to send A Squadron with mine clearance equipment. The tanks secured the site of the attack, and their night-fighting capability made them an essential addition to the security forces on the spot. Or as Lee Windsor, David Charters, and Brent Wilson put it in their book "Kandahar Tour": "No one on that wretched night in the desert near Ghundey Ghar questioned the value of deploying tanks to Afghanistan." (Windsor, L., et al., 2008, p. 133). There were no further attacks on Canadian forces on that night of April 11-12.

As the poppy harvest came to an end in early May, it was clear to the Canadians that they had to expect increasing efforts by the Taliban to attack ISAF troops or Afghan security authorities. Not only had they been spreading the news on all communication channels for months that they wanted to take back Kandahar this year, but after the poppy harvest, many Afghans would be out of work and would therefore be recruited by the Taliban as so-called Tier 2 fighters. The Canadian battle group wanted to prevent renewed attacks by stepping up its patrolling activities in the western part of the Nalgham-Sangsar region west of Kandahar and intensively searching for IEDs. To this end, the Leos and their mine rollers were deployed and commanded by Broomfield's deputy Captain Craig Volstad (call sign T1A). Other than mine plows, mine rollers do not destroy the infrastructure while searching for explosive ordnances. In order to deceive the insurgents, mine rollers were separately transferred by truck to Patrol Base (PB) Wilson. In the early morning hours of May 7, 2007, the Canadian tankers mounted the mine rollers on two of their Leopard tanks under the protection of the Zahri District Center walls. The equipped tanks were commanded by Sergeants Sewards (call sign T12B) and Jordison (call sign T16). Before sunrise, the tanks left the base as part of a column consisting of Hotel Company (again Alex Ruff), a Badger armored engineer vehicle (AEV), and two ANA platoons.

Jordison took the foremost position of the column. It moved along Highway 1 to Howz-e-Madad, where it turned south towards Nalgham. After only a few hundred meters along a narrow dirt road walled in on both sides, two RPG missiles detonated in front of Jordison. The sergeant stopped his tank as more RPGs were fired from another position and a machine gun began shooting. This time the enemy fire was directed at a civilian jungle truck traveling on Highway 1 on behalf of the U.S. Armed Forces. It got hit several times, and one occupant was killed. Parts of Hotel Company dismounted from their vehicles to engage the Taliban when yet another missile missed Jordison's tank by a hair's breadth. His gunner spotted a man in black headgear in

51

some sort of emplacement ahead along the dirt road. But it was not until he fired another RPG that they could be sure it was one of the attackers. The missile detonated 20 meters ahead of Jordison. His tank returned fire with a HESH round (which disperses plastic explosives over the target on impact before it detonates), eliminating the attacker and his emplacement. After that, the firefight died away for the time being. The column was denied permission to break out of the road walled into the offside fields to gain more room to move. ISAF leadership did not want to risk any trouble with the population due to destroyed fields. But then Jordison's tank reported four Taliban fighters in a grape hut located along the dirt road. However, there were still civilians in the sightline, hastily seeking cover. Jordison's waited until his gunner could get a clear shot with the coaxial machine gun. At the same time, Ruff's dismounted infantrymen approached the enemy. The column was then again fired upon from the front as well as from the southeast. Two RPG missiles flew right over Volstad's tank, at which point the captain ordered the column to break out of the walled road to the left. His gunner shot opened that very wall with one HESH round. First, the Badger with its pre-stressed dozer blade pushed through the breach in order to cut a lane into the adjacent grape field. Leopards and LAV followed, thus gaining more room to move and a better overview of the battlefield. However, shortly after that, both the Badger AEV and Jordison's Leo got stuck in the well irrigated field. Within minutes they were pulled out by the other Leopard tanks, but Volstad concluded that the field was not a suitable alternative route to Nalgham. On the one hand, the column would destroy valuable grape harvests and irrigation systems in its further advance. On the other hand, the Canadians had to expect to get stuck even more often – and under enemy fire.

Once again, Volstad was fired at by RPG shooters, who had barricaded themselves behind an earth wall some 300 meters away. Since his intercom malfunctioned (the interior of his Leopard had heated up to 60 degrees Celsius due to the heat of that day, more on this later), he had to shout his orders through the fighting compartment. The gunner first fired a HESH shell at the earth wall. When a Taliban fighter with an RPG fled, he was killed with a second round.

Major Ruff felt that the Taliban were trying to lure his combat team further down the road to Nalgham. He, therefore, ordered the retreat to PB Wilson in the afternoon. But first, the Badger AEV repaired a damaged irrigation ditch. During the fighting, six Taliban fighters were killed and two captured. No civilians were injured. Two Canadian tankers had collapsed due to the enormous heat generated in the tanks during the operation and needed medical treatment. Special cooling suits had already been requested but were still on their way to Afghanistan on that May 7.

In coordination with the battle group, said column made another attempt to reach Nalgham the very next day – this time via a different route. On the morning of May 8, 2007, the column with Sergeant Sewards' tank at the foremost position, left the base, took Highway 1, passed the point where it had turned south the day before, and finally turned onto a road leading to Ghundey Ghar. The Canadian-Afghan combat team reached the southwest of Nalgham, known for its landscape of vast fields. There they first deployed into a leaguer. Most of the fields here had been harvested so that the combat team could advance to the village off the road. A villager warned the soldiers about mines or IEDs along the road, so the pioneers were deployed.

Meanwhile, Sewards also began clearing an alternative route to Nalgham using mine rollers. Several Taliban fighters fired on the Canadians from buildings with assault rifles and RPGs. One missile hit a Canadian Army Mercedes-Benz Bison recovery vehicle and severely damaged it. The combat team returned fire. Dismounted infantry prepared to storm the buildings.

Meanwhile, one Leo and three LAVs moved south from the leaguer to establish a second firing position from which they could guard any push on Nalgham. At that time, Sewards spotted a four-man Taliban squad on the roof of a grape hut, operating two RPGs and a Kalashnikov. With one shot from the 105-millimeter gun, his gunner blew up the roof. The man with the Kalashnikov survived, but was then gunned down with the coaxial MG.

Together with the dismounted ANA infantry, Volstad pushed forward, as he followed the Afghans at a distance of 100 meters. In doing so, he identified a Taliban squad with an 82-millimeter anti-tank recoilless gun, which he destroyed with two shots from the main armament by overshooting the ANA infantrymen. More Taliban showed up and were combated by the ANA forces and the Canadian Leopards. As the operation progressed, more RPG squads were taken out while Dutch Apache helicopters provided air support. Several Taliban used civilians as human shields by entrenching themselves in their homes. The Canadians and Afghans avoided shooting at those insurgents. The day finally ended with about a dozen Taliban fighters killed. There were no civilian casualties.

In mid-May, Canadian Leopard 1 C2s occupied an elevation at Ghundey Ghar, supporting a Canadian-Portuguese operation directed against suspected Taliban forces in Kolk.

On May 17, 2007, the well-known combat team under the command of Major Ruff and with the participation of Volstad's tanks equipped with mine rollers and dozer blades made another advance on Nalgham, this time coming from the southwest. Taliban troops quickly opened fire with automatic weapons and RPG. Several Leos formed a leaguer while dismounted infantry soldiers pushed towards enemy positions. Along with a platoon from Hotel Company, Volstad's tank made a breakthrough south of a suspected ambush on the main road. The Taliban quickly retreated toward Nalgham so that the Canadians could hold a meeting with the local elders.

On May 18, 2007, the combat team, now reinforced by an Afghan police unit, approached Nalgham from the north. Dismounted infantry checked the buildings along the access road. The Leo with call sign T11A (Warrant Officer Pudar) took over the column's lead with pre-stressed mine rollers. Similar to May 7, this road was walled in on both sides. Broad fields adjoined the low clay walls. Pudar's mine rollers finally hit a powerful IED, which in the explosion tore a meter-deep crater into the dirt road. The mine rollers intercepted the explosion's blast as planned, leaving the tank and crew mostly unharmed and still fully operational. Shortly after that, the column was again fired upon by Taliban riflemen and RPG shooters. At this time, Volstad, along with the Badger and other forces in platoon strength, bypassed the ambush site to the south, while a second platoon secured the road to the north. The Afghan police searched the buildings along the road. Talks with residents revealed that the Taliban had set up a killing zone for ISAF forces on the road ahead. After further small skirmishes, the heat reached record levels again around noon. A LAV, which was supposed to bring additional drinking water, got off the cleared lane by only centimeters, and hit a mine. The detonation did not wound anyone but caused all the water bottles to burst, so the operation had to be aborted.

A week later, the entire staff of the battle group moved to a checkpoint at Ma'Sum Ghar in preparation for a major offensive against the Taliban at Nalgham-Sangsar, which included all forces of the battle group, Portuguese commandos, and the 2nd Afghan Kandak/1st Brigade/205th Corps. The staff of the Kandak also set up in Ma'Sum Ghar for this purpose. Broomfield had returned from leave and participated in the operation but left the tactical command to Volstad.

At the start of the operation, Canadians, Portuguese, and Afghans began to draw a ring around Nalgham. Hotel Company, mechanized engineers, three ANA companies, and two troops of Broomfield's tanks, moved to an area north of the AO, and from there, once from north to south, combed the Taliban-controlled terrain. They moved along wadis and overcame them with fascines in order to eliminate suspected Taliban ambush positions before tanks with mine rollers advanced over the roads. Volstad moved into position at the eastern end of the formation when his tank disappeared in a colossal explosion plume caused by an IED made of three tank mines. All crew members survived the attack, slightly wounded. They switched to a replacement tank and continued the offensive.

The leader of the Canadian Operational Mentor and Liaison Team (OMLT) that trained the Afghans discovered another IED on the road shortly afterward. He was still trying to warn the Leopard in his back when the explosive device detonated. The OMLT leader himself, a

Portuguese, and an interpreter were wounded in the incident. However, one Canadian soldier did not survive the strike. Nevertheless, the operation was continued and completed after a few contacts with the enemy.

All in all, it can be said that the Leopard 1 C2 had been increasingly deployed in close-quarter combat against insurgents since May 2007 in joint operations with other mechanized forces, supported by artillery and from the air, and achieved several decisive victories in the Zhari district – and that in areas that are hardly accessible for wheeled vehicles due to dense fields and confusing building complexes. Tanks and Canadian and Afghan infantry respectively advanced side by side against Taliban positions in Howz-e-Madad, Nalgham, and Sangsar.

In late May/early June 2007, Canadian troops were attacked near Kolk. Lieutenant Wilson and his 8 Platoon came under AK, MG, and RPG fire in the afternoon. Lieutenant Jun's 7 Platoon and one Leo went out to reinforce them. While still on the march, they were fired upon from a hut by a group of Taliban. The tank responded with its 105-millimeter main armament. The detonation destroyed the hut. Meanwhile, Wilson's unit was able to put the enemy to flight under its own steam.

In the morning hours of the following day, the Taliban attacked an ANA company north of Sangsar. A fierce firefight developed. The attached Canadian OMLT called for reinforcements. The Taliban were pinned down by ANA fire, so the battle group decided to eliminate them with a flank attack accompanied by a U.S. airstrike. For that flank attack, mechanized sappers and Leopard tanks under the command of Captain Volstad were selected.

When the Taliban detected the approaching Canadian tanks, they set off towards an uninhabited plain. Two A-10 Thunderbolts rushed on and fired on the insurgents, this attack being coordinated by the Canadian Forward Air Controller, Captain Ryan Sheppard. Then ANA forces counterattacked and took prisoner six Taliban fighters.

On the night of June 4, 2007, India Company and one ANA company infiltrated the village of Siah Choy in Zahri near the Arghandāb River to hold a shura with the village elders at daybreak. Strathcona's tanks helped to secure access to that village.

Early in the morning, India Company was attacked and pinned down by a Taliban platoon on the way back. Close combat broke out; the two parties were only meters apart. The Canadians called for artillery and air support. Broomfield's tanks were in the vicinity as a quick reaction force, and they got moving immediately. With fascines, they overcame a wadi and then shot walls to shreds that were blocking their way. The Taliban platoon was finally defeated, killing four or five insurgents. The Canadians suffered no casualties. They had the damage to infrastructure, and private property repaired immediately.

Throughout June, the Canadian Leos assisted when India Company and the 2nd Kandak of the ANA visited villages in Zhari District suspected of being Taliban-held. The Leos secured those villages by cutting them off from the outside and often came into contact with fleeing insurgents.

Furthermore, in June 2007, Hotel Company and Canadian Leopards patrolled the north of Kandahar Province (in the districts Khakrez and Shah Wali Kot) to expand the so-called Afghan Development Zone, which testifies to how much the few tanks were deployed in the whole area of responsibility. At the request of the U.S.-Americans, the combat team provided additional support in the fight for Khakrez in mid-June.

On the night of June 20, 2007, India Company, supported by Afghan forces from 2nd Kandak, infiltrated Howz-e-Madad to challenge a suspected Taliban company, including an IED cell. To the south, Captain Volstad combed the area with a troop of tanks and other ANA forces. The goal was to meet India Company at a roadblock set up by them. In the said village, close combat broke out between Canadians, the ANA, and the Taliban, with American and Dutch aircrafts launching airstrikes.

In the course of a Taliban offensive that began on June 18, 2007, against ANP posts in the far north in Ghorak and Mianashin, Hotel Company and the mass of Leopard tanks in Afghanistan under the command of Broomfield formed a combat team that moved out to Padah, where the point of main effort of the enemy attack was believed to be. Captain Eric Angel also commanded a Leo troop on the left flank, which joined forces with mechanized sappers, a platoon from India Company, and a sniper fire team to recapture the Ghorak district center. On the right flank, Canadian recce troops joined Afghan police forces.

The Broomfield combat team ran into company size Taliban forces on the outskirts of Padah. The enemy had established himself along a wadi in trenches and shelters and some houses for defense. Yet another battle developed, reminiscent of a conventional war: at 09:00 hrs, the attacking Canadians were fired at with RPGs. They opened up with all their weapons, including the Leos' main armament and machine guns. Fighting took place at close range as well as at distances of up to 2,000 meters. Canadian artillery also fired at insurgent positions. U.S. helicopters finally landed commandos behind the Taliban to prevent them from fleeing. After two hours of fierce fighting, 40 insurgents were dead, 20 of them killed by Hotel Company and Broomfield's tanks.

This event was followed by a week of ferocious battles in which the Canadians and U.S. commandos operated as an autonomous combat group. Ghorak, Mianashin, and Gumbad were liberated in the course of the fighting. The Canadian Air Force dropped supplies over the battlefield, and Crabbs' unit provided the tankers everything they needed. Nevertheless, profound wear and tear on the decrepit tanks could not be denied. According to Windsor et al., the operations at the end of June showed the Canadian tankers that the life span of their Leopard 1 C2 was nearing its end. Maintaining the Leos' operational capability was becoming an ever-greater challenge. The wear and tear after about nine months in the dust of Afghanistan took its toll. The main problem was the simultaneous deployment of Leos at different locations in the area of responsibility. For example, in addition to patrol duties, tanks had to be part of the quick reaction force.

A Squadron was to provide two tanks to an infantry company to lead an attack on Taliban forces threatening an Afghan National Police station in an undated event. However, at that time, all of the mine rollers and plows were in use elsewhere. The two tanks' crews were thus forced to create safe lanes in potential mine- and booby trap infested areas by simply rolling over them, driven by the quiet hope of surviving possible detonations in their armored vehicles. A little later, one of the two tanks got stuck in a wadi. The second one tried to pull it out, but it failed. Consequently, the infantry had to secure the area until a sapper unit could move in and recover the Leopards.

In the early hours of July 4, 2007, the Canadian battle group launched an attack in Zalakhan to neutralize an IED cell. Canadian mechanized infantry, artillery observers, and snipers surrounded the village before a Canadian-Afghan column rolled towards it via the only access road. The column was led by Leopard tanks with pre-stressed mine rollers respectively dozer blades. A recovery tank accompanied them. ANA and ANP forces, Canadian engineers, military police, and mechanized recce troops were also part of the mentioned column. The Taliban avoided any confrontation. Hours later, the column drove back and was struck by a powerful IED hidden deep in the dirt road and consisted of several agglomerated artillery shells and anti-tank mines. The triggerman let the Leopard tanks pass and detonated the explosive device when an RG-31 Nyala armored infantry mobility vehicle approached. The explosion lifted the Nyala, which weighs several tons, high into the air. The vehicle hit the ground again, smashed to pieces. The one Afghan and six Canadian occupants were dead instantly. The Triggerman and his team were taken into custody on site.

Hotel Company and the Leopards served as a fire brigade for the entire area of responsibility during and after the liberation of Ghorak, Mianashin, and Gumbad. On July 8, 2007, a call for help reached them from Ghorak, where strong Taliban forces besieged the local police. An ANP convoy with supplies and reinforcements had been ambushed on the way to Ghorak, and the ANP men had been beheaded. Simultaneously, like the Canadians, the 3rd Kandak of the 1st Brigade also started to move via Dutch helicopters to Ghorak. They managed to get the Taliban to flee and to appease the town again. In the village, however, marked by signs of battle, the Canadians, including Broomfield's tankers, made a terrible discovery: the Taliban had kidnapped and decapitated a 10-year-old boy who had been cooking for the ANP men and exhibited his head and body publicly in the village as a warning.

On July 10, 2007, a Leopard 1 C2 took the convoy's rearmost position when an IED detonated at the side of the road before insurgents opened fire from handguns. Two crew members of that Leo were wounded from the explosion. The incident occurred 25 kilometers east of Kandahar.

Later in July 2007, the Canadian battle group participated in Operation Porter, an ANP operation to secure terrorist material in the Panjwai district. The perpetrators of the July 4 attack were suspected to be in Nakhonay, a neighboring village of Zalakhan, and were to be arrested in this operation. The Canadian Leopards, among others, secured the perimeter for this operation by blocking main access roads. A Leo raiding party broke into walls and cleared safe lanes to the village, which were then used by the forces that were moving in. No battle emerged, but the ANP was able to seize war material and arrest several suspects.

In late summer, Broomfield's tankers took part in skirmishes at Ghundey Ghar before heading home as part of the rotation change.

Major Cadieu reports on attacks with IEDs, mines, and RPGs on Canadian Leopards, as well as attacks by suicide bombers, which is not explicitly mentioned in any other source. Since at the time he published his report, the deployment of Leopard 2 A6Ms was imminent, I assume that his text covers the period until early summer 2007. Furthermore, Cadieu estimates the number of insurgents killed by Leopard 1 C2s in the first nine months of their deployment at several dozen.

In summary, the Leopards had different tasks in combined arms operations: escorting columns, fire support for the infantry, guarding tasks, counter-mine and counter-IED operations, and point of main effort attacks to penetrate enemy positions. Using HESH ammunition, Leopard crews punched five by five-meter holes in clay huts and fought dismounted forces at a combat distance of 150 to 4,000 meters. Mine rollers and mine plows detonated IEDs that were triggered by pressure plates. Cadieu, therefore, does not see the main battle tank as a pure means of fighting enemy tanks, but rather as an instrument with which the tactical freedom of movement can be maintained or increased with relatively little risk. Leopard 1 C2s helped clear minefields and IED traps, flatten walls and penetrate dense grape and marijuana fields. Tanks secured the outer perimeter for operations by other troops and forced access to embattled areas to recover, for example, wounded, dead and material.

Cadieu also shares his thoughts on the costs of maintaining the Leopard fleet in Afghanistan. His conclusion: "The only guarantee when employing armour in the harsh environment of Afghanistan is that tanks will break." (Cadieu, T., 2008, p. 13). Engines failed due to dust exposure, and the hydraulic turret drive went on strike when overheating. Maintenance and repair of the tanks proved to be too costly and time-consuming, and the situation of spare parts was tense, which quickly made the Canadian Leos a scarce resource for the troops. As a result, the tank force was the only Canadian arm of the service supported by a dedicated supply unit of the National Support Element during the ISAF mission. This unit provided operating supplies, ammunition, spare parts, a mobile recovery team, and an ambulance. The supply echelon had mechanized elements itself. Thus it was able to fight independently and could be deployed without outside help throughout the entire AoR.

Nevertheless, ensuring the operational capability of MBTs operating simultaneously at different locations was a significant challenge and remained a bottleneck in the Leopard's operations. It should be emphasized here that the supply unit mentioned above initially consisted of tankers who had a proper understanding of the needs of their weapon system. However, in the course of the ISAF mission, the NSE decided to replace them with regular drivers.

Cadieu also discusses the aspect of strategic transport, arguing that an army must build up its own air transport capabilities for global deployment of armored forces. In 2006, the Canadian armed forces were not yet ready and had to resort to allies or leased private aircraft space. However, a fiasco like that with KFOR did not happen.

In fact, the Leopard 1 proved to be a valuable brother-in-arms of the Canadian forces and their allies in Afghanistan, not only because of its firepower but also because of its ability to clear obstacles with dozer blades or the tank's sheer weight, thus paving the way for other units. Then again, there are apparent deficits, one of the most significant of which is the lack of air conditioning, which makes service in a Leopard 1 in Afghanistan's heat comparable to sitting in a boiler on an open flame. 50 degrees Celsius outside temperature quickly turn into a life-threatening 60 to 65 degrees Celsius in the fighting compartment of a Leo. This panzer was designed for Central European environmental conditions, so special cooling suits were subsequently procured for the Canadian ISAF crews. These suits were available from mid-2007. The hydraulic turret engine also generates considerable heat, which contributes to the internal temperature. The horrendous temperatures caused the tankers to produce so much sweat that electronic components increasingly failed due to short circuits – the failure of Volstad's intercom on May 7, 2007, was probably also caused in this way. Since the tanks were needed daily, air conditioning systems based on the Australian model were out of the question. As a result, operations involving Leopard were usually carried out at night or in the early morning hours.

Also, the protection factor of the Leo 1 remains limited compared to more modern battle tanks. Despite all upgrades, IED strikes or RPG fire remain real dangers for the crew of a Leopard 1.

Furthermore, the aspect of collateral damage must be considered. There is no evidence of collateral damage among the civilian population caused by Leopard 1 tanks. Further, firing a tank equipped with a fire control computer proves to be more targeted than bombardment from the air or artillery. However, the Leo's tracks occasionally caused damage to the infrastructure. Canadian pioneers tried to repair the damage as far as possible after operations.

The mission in Afghanistan ultimately led to a rethink within the Canadian armed forces. Instead of abolishing their tank force, old Leopard 1 panzers were reactivated and upgraded in a rush – and later replaced by the Leopard 2, of which the first 20 were also procured in a rush (more on this below). When these arrived in Kandahar in the summer of 2007, it became quiet around the Leopard 1 C2 at the Hindu Kush, whose number was soon reduced to six. However, by the end of 2009, they were still being used to guard areas, mostly at elevated positions near a camp. The tank crews were provided throughout by the men and women of Lord Strathcona's Horse.

Leos in attempted Coup d'état in Turkey

In the course of the attempted coup, the renegade military sent at least three Leopard 1s together with three other armored vehicles to Istanbul's Atatürk Airport in the night from July 15 to July 16, 2016, shortly before 23:00 hrs. In this context, the photo of the so-called #Tankman gained worldwide attention. The man in question was Metin Doğan, a civilian who lay down in front of an approaching Leopard 1 tank to prevent it from continuing its mission while soldiers threatened to shoot Doğan. The driver of the Leos stopped his tank just in time.

If the restaurant owner Mehmet Sükrukintas is to be believed, he and others went to the airport on the night of the coup attempt, where they obstructed the way of some tanks (probably the mentioned Leopard 1s). According to Sükrukintas, some undressed up to their underwear and stuffed the clothes into the tanks' exhaust pipes. This measure brought the tanks to a halt a few minutes later. The soldiers opened the hatches, and civilians pulled them out.

In addition to the proven use of Leopard main battle tanks at the Atatürk Airport, Tagesschau (German newscast) also mentions tanks patrolling the streets of Ankara and Istanbul. The statement is underlined by pictures of Leopard 1s driving along a main road in the dark. It can be assumed that the editors of Tagesschau do not differentiate distinctly between tank types. It is also unclear which road is shown; it could be an access road to the airport. Whether Leopard 1 tanks operated in Ankara and the city of Istanbul during that night cannot be conclusively determined based on the given sources.

References for this Chapter

For the episode around Dagmar Lill, I recommend studying the corresponding Spiegel article from 1994. Hodge discusses the use of Leopard 1s against the PKK; for further reading, see Grässlin (2013) and Aliza Marcus (2007) as well as Human Rights Watch (1995).

Compare Kim Sørensen's "The Leopard 1 in Danish Service" (2020), which discusses all operations of Danish Leopard 1s. Further, see Hansen (undated). I took the Danish terms of military unit sizes and ranks from my e-mail correspondence with Thomas Antonsen.

On the website of the Leopard Club (undated), photos of Belgian Leopard 1 in action can be found. Moreover, Verboven (2014) states that Belgium has also deployed the Leopard 1 in the territory of former Yugoslavia. Further reading: Dederichs (2001), Bron Pancerna (2015), as well as Wikipédia (undated) – the latter is of course hardly acceptable as a source, but there simply is no other.

I want to recommend Frank Lobitz's publication (2009), in which he also treats the Leopard 1 here and there. Canada's involvement in Kosovo is discussed in detail in Maloney (2019), where a Canadian tank troop structure is also described. For Operation Determined Effort, see Government of Canada (2018). The deployment of the Canadian Leopard 1 at the Hindu Kush is treated by Defense Industry Daily (2014). For further reading, see Walter Håland's article (2012) in the Austrian magazine TRUPPENDIENST and the listing made by Canadian American Strategic Review (undated), also Schulze (2010a), (2010b) and (2015) and Trevor Cadieu (2008) as well as Windsor et al. As for Windsor, the book takes an overly optimistic view of all Canadian activities in Afghanistan and, although it is a textbook, its descriptions sometimes drift into the realm of fictional works. For Operation Baaz Tzuka, see NATO (2006). Operation Achilles is discussed by Gunther Hauser (2008) and Thomas Frankenfeld (2009). For the operation of December 21, 2006, see Finlayson (2008). For early operations in November 2006, see Horn (2010).

The #Tankman is treated by Anna Kröning (2016), see also Tagesschau (2016), Heinrich (2016) and Triebert (2016) for the coup d'état attempt.

The Leopard 2

Leopard 2 A6

Description

As the general contractor, Krauss-Maffei was responsible for developing the Leopard 2, with Porsche, Wegmann, and Krupp MaK all played a significant role. Krauss-Maffei and Krupp MaK carried out the final assembly and delivery of the series version tanks. Now new Leopard 2s are produced in Germany by Krauss-Maffei Wegmann, a 1999 merger of Krauss-Maffei and Wegmann. Besides, the Leopard 2 has often been manufactured abroad under license.

The **Leopard 2 (also Leopard 2 A0) series version** is equipped with a 12-cylinder MB 873 Ka-500 diesel engine, which is derived from the KPz 70 development and, in a modified design with turbocharger and intercooling, generates 1,500 hp. It enables the Leo 2 to cover a distance of slightly more than 20 meters from a standing start within five seconds, more than doubling its acceleration performance compared to its older brother. The top speed is 68 kilometers per hour forward and 31 kilometers per hour backward. With around 450 kilometers, the operational range is less than that of the Leopard 1, but the Leo 2 also carries around 15 tons more weight. The series version weighs 55 tons. Furthermore, the tank can climb 1.1 meters, run up gradients of up to 60 percent, and overcome trenches up to three meters wide. It can cross waters up to a depth of four meters without much preparation.

In the development of the Leopard 2, the protection factor has been given high priority. At that time, armoring technologies were available that promised protection against shaped charges. Special attention was also paid to protection against mines. All of this eventually resulted in grading the Leo 2 as Military Load Classification 60, which means additional effort and additional costs in terms of logistics.

The Leopard 2's main armament is a 120-millimeter smoothbore L/44 gun from Rheinmetall, for which fin-stabilized balancing ammunition as well as multi-purpose ammunition with a shaped charge and fragmentation effects (thus also usable against soft targets; for the sake of simplicity, I will also refer to it as HEAT rounds in the following) were developed. One cartridge weighs no more than its 105-millimeter counterpart of the Leo 1. Later, other types of ammunition were added by the various users of the Leo 2, including canister ammunition and High-Explosive rounds. The correlation range finder (a combination of optical and laser-based measurement) in the EMES 15 target device brings together both systems' advantages. The result of the measurement is fed into the fire control computer, which processes numerous variables influencing the shot and thus determines the values for predicted fire and displays them to the user in analog respectively digital form. The optics are primarily stabilized. A gyro-stabilized turret drive system adjusts the main gun's barrel with the movements of the tank. (Perhaps you are familiar with the video of the Leopard 2, which at full speed balances a glass of beer on the tip of its main gun without spilling anything). The electrical connection of the target device with the main armament, combined with the above mentioned components, provides an excellent first hit probability from a standing position and driving. The thermal imaging device integrated into the EMES 15 was not yet available for series production when the first Leopard 2 A0s were delivered; therefore, those vehicles were equipped with a residual light amplifier instead. The Leopard 2 is considered the first German main battle tank to be altogether night fighting capable. Another tactical advantage, especially over the Russian T-models, is that the gun can be lowered very far. The Leo 2 can penetrate the turret armor of a T-62 at over 4,000 meters, while the mentioned East Bloc tank would have to approach 1,000 meters to achieve the same with the Leo 2. The stand-by ammunition in the turret consists of 15 rounds. As secondary armament, the Leopard 2 is equipped with an MG 3 parallel to the axis of the cannon and an MG 3 next to the loading hatch as an anti-aircraft mean. Like the Leopard 1, its successor is equipped with a smoke mortar system.

The Leopard 2 has room for four crew members: commander, gunner, loader, and driver. A passive night vision device is available for the driver.

In a guest article in Krapke's publication, the former Oberstleutnant and commander of the Panzerlehrbatallion (tank training battalion), Reinhold Schulenburg, judges that the Leopard 2 is the right answer to the quantitative superiority of the Warsaw Pact since a tank troop equipped with this very panzer is capable of fighting aggressively and proactively on its own and thereby demonstrating its superiority in duel situations.

In addition, the Leo 2 is considered to be outstanding in maintenance issues. This panzer is also certified as having further potential for upgrades and adaptation and thus an even longer life in active service. In any case, it is remarkable that the Leopard 2 is still in production after more than 40 years and is being further developed at great expense.

References for this Chapter

My description of the Leopard 2 is mainly based on Krapke (1984) and Zwilling (2018a). Additionally, Zwilling (2020), where I recommend reading the preface of Rolf Hilmes regarding the evaluation of the Leo 2. I took the operational range from the website of Krauss-Maffei Wegmann (undated, b). The video with the glass of beer can be admired at ViralTimeLapse (2015).

Upgrades

In the early 1980s, the **Leopard 2 A1** was released. The most significant change is the standard installation of the thermal imaging device in the main periscope. It replaces the residual light amplifier. The crosswind sensor is also omitted. Other improvements include, depending on the production batch, the NBC scoop, the electrics, the ammunition bracket for the main armament, footsteps on the engine block, modifications to the commander's periscope and the exhaust gas gratings, a port for the field cable on the turret, and changes in the arrangement of the tow ropes, to the tank filler neck and some coverings. Besides, modifications were made to the fighting compartment on some vehicles of this upgrade.

The series version tanks were retrofitted with the thermal imaging device in the main periscope, thus removing the residual light amplifier, making them the upgrade variant **Leopard 2 A2**.

The **Leopard 2 A3** comes with a new SEM 80/90 radio and, for the first time, with a three-color camouflage paint job.

The **Leopard 2 A4** has a combat weight of 55 tons with a deadweight of 52 tons, whereby different vehicles with slightly different features are summarized under this variant designation. The Leopard 2 A4's main feature is the digital ballistics system for the fire control computer, which can calculate additional types of ammunition, among other things. Furthermore, the A4s are partly equipped with a fire suppression system in the fighting compartment, with a more user-friendly paint job, with additional armor plates on the turret and hull front, new batteries, tracks, side skirts, and idler wheel covers, as well as a field adjustment mirror for the main gun. The ammunition hatch on the left side of the turret is also removed.

Under the premise of improving survivability and maneuverability, the **Leopard 2 A5** was finally developed. In this variant, the turret front and sides are fitted with new, sloped armor modules, giving the vehicle a slightly futuristic look that will continue to distinguish the Leopard 2 in later upgrades. Inside the turret, the walls are clad with spall liners, which significantly improve protection against shrapnel. Besides further improvements such as modified hatches, track faceplates, and more, the reversing aid for the driver including a monitor is worth mentioning, as well as the integration of an OPHELIOS thermal imaging device in the commander's panoramic periscope and the installation of a purely electric turret drive system and a purely electric emergency adjustment drive. The laser range finder is also improved, and a hybrid navigation system is installed – the combat weight increases to almost 60 tons. For the Leo 2 A5, an urban camouflage scheme has been developed for combat in built-up areas.

The **Leopard 2 A6** upgrade focuses on firepower. The L/55, for example, is an improved and 1.30 meters longer main armament of the same caliber. Further, performance-enhanced KE ammunition was introduced with this variant. With the A6 upgrade, the combat weight exceeds the 60 ton mark for the first time, albeit by only 500 kilograms.

With the **Leopard 2 A6M,** the German Armed Forces responded to their experience since 1999 in Kosovo and Macedonia. Accordingly, vehicles of this variant are equipped with additional mine protection. The combat weight is thus 62.5 tons. Other modifications were also fitted in addition to the mine protection, including improved seats, coverings over the front torsion bars, new ammunition brackets, a new slip ring assembly, and a new turret rotating platform. The stowage concept for the onboard equipment was also changed. Later, the combat effectiveness of the A6M was further improved by a new thermal imaging device, a new intercom, a fire suppression system in the turret, new control panels, and the installation of ultracaps on the fighting compartment roof.

The Leopard **2 A6MA2** is based on the Dutch Leo 2 A6, which is equipped with the Dutch digital battlefield management system. It remains unclear whether this upgrade has the additional protection package from the A6M variant. The name suggests this, but I can't find any source proving that Dutch 2 A6 tanks have been upgraded accordingly.

The **Leopard 2 A7** is another fundamental upgrade. Thanks to the integration of the Integrated Command and Information System IFIS, the A7 is at the cutting edge of tactical command and control. An electrics and fighting compartment cooling system was installed, making the tank suitable for all climate zones. The Leo 2 A7 is modified to the extent that it can fire Rheinmetall's advanced DM11 ammunition, whose fuse can be set to impact, delayed detonation, or airburst. In addition, the commander's panoramic periscope was given a new thermal image, and a new intercom with an outside phone has also been installed. Optimization of the onboard power supply system, new controls, and a fire suppression system in the turret complete a significant increase in combat effectiveness. The combat weight thus grows to a whopping 64.1 tons with an empty weight of 61.9 tons. This harms acceleration, which must be ensured by the drive train that has remained unchanged in its core since 1979.

In 2017, minor improvements were introduced to variant A7. The crew's hand weapons are now stowed on the turret roof for faster access, and further changes have been made to the stowage concept. Besides, the driver received a reading lamp, and the loader's seat was replaced.

The **Leopard 2 A7V variant** (with which the circle to the first German battle tank A7V produced in series is intentionally or coincidentally closed) was developed, among other things, base on the experiences that the Canadians and Danes made with their Leos 2 in Afghanistan. The A7V features more ergonomic seats, a new thermal imaging device in the gunner's scope, a night-vision capable front and rearview camera, an improved air conditioning system including NBC protection ventilation as well as additional armor plates. An improved laser range finder further increases the probability of a first shot hit. Modifications to the transmission, the gear ratio, the torsion bars, and new tracks improve acceleration performance while reducing top speed. A new commander's monitor, new digital control elements, and other detailed improvements complete the A7V's combat effectiveness.

Krauss-Maffei Wegmann combined the 2 A7 and 2 A7V variants' modifications with further detailed improvements in the **Leopard 2A7+**. The focus is on protective components for the crew, including improved turret armor and mine protection in the hull. An FLW 200 weapon station with a .50-MG or 40-millimeter automatic grenade launcher is mounted on the turret, which can be operated from the fighting compartment's safety.

References for this Chapter

This chapter is based on Zwilling (2018a) and (2018b) and Lobitz (2009). For the DM11, I refer to the website of Rheinmetall Defence (2017). For the early Leopard 2 variants, I rely on Zwilling (2020), Spielberger (1995), and Schulze (2020). For the Leo 2 A7+, see Krauss-Maffei Wegmann (undated, c). The Dutch special variant can be found at Twigt (2018).

Users

At the end of the 1970s, the Bundesministerium der Verteidigung (Federal Ministry of Defence) of the Federal Republic of **Germany** ordered a total of 1,800 Leopard 2's. Most vehicles of this order were delivered with the first four production batches. The first batch consisted of the series version (380 in total), the second and third batches were of Leopard 2 A1s (750 in total). And in the fourth batch, 300 Leopard 2 A3 were produced. These were handed over to the troops by the end of 1985. The tanks of the series version were subsequently upgraded to the A2 upgrade package. Between 1985 and 1992, the German Armed Forces received 695 additional Leopard 2 A4s in four production batches, some with slightly different levels of equipment. Germany procured a total of 2,125 Leopard 2 main battle tanks of the variants A0 to A4, with all older versions being upgraded to A4 during the course of their service. (Rolf Hilmes speaks in his 2011 publication of a total of 2,225 Leos – I assume that this is a typo, as it contradicts all other sources by exactly 100 vehicles). The last tank straight from the factory was delivered to the Bundeswehr on March 19, 1992.

A total of 285 Leos were upgraded to the A5 variant from 1995 onwards, of which less than 20 have remained in the German Army today. Starting in 2001, 160 Leo 2 A5s were upgraded to the A6 variant, 65 Leopard A4s were upgraded to that variant too. Between 2004 and 2008, 70 panzers were upgraded to the A6M configuration. The Leo 2 A4 was taken out of service until 2008. Since December 2014, the Heer has received 20 Leopard 2 A7s, followed by the first Leo 2 A7V in October 2019. It is planned to procure 104 tanks of this type by 2023. 51 units of the A6 variant and 50 A6Ms have been/will be upgraded to the A7V variant from March 2019 onwards.

The Bundeswehr plans to increase its Leopard 2 fleet to a total of 320 vehicles by 2025, equipping each battalion with one uniform variant. It is also expected that the German Army will keep a double-digit number of additional tanks in their inventory for testing and retrofitting purposes. The particular case of German-Dutch cooperation in the field of tanks is dealt with in the following section on the Netherlands.

After a sample tank had already been delivered for testing purposes, the **Netherlands** was the first non-German customer to receive a total of 445 Leopard 2 A1 main battle tanks (as Leopard 2 NL) with slight modifications between 1981 and 1986: The secondary armament was replaced with Belgian MAG machine guns, another intercom and other radios including antennas were installed, and Dutch smoke mortars were mounted. In the following years, all vehicles were upgraded to the A4 variant (the Dutch adopted the German designations and just added NL). However, the fire suppression system in the fighting compartment was not installed.

From 1996, 180 main battle tanks were upgraded to the A5 variant with minimal modifications (among others, mounting of modified side skirts was renounced), and between 2001 and 2004, they were further upgraded to A6. With each upgrade, the Leos retained the national modifications described above.

Following numerous army structural reforms with a steady reduction in the number of combat troops, the Netherlands still had 60 active Leopard 2s in 2009. In 2011, the Dutch government announced that its armed forces would in the future dispense entirely with their tank force as part of austerity measures. The remaining 60 Leopard 2s were decommissioned. Only four years later, Germany and the Netherlands intensified their binational military cooperation: the Dutch 43 Gemechaniseerde Brigade (= 43rd Mechanized Brigade) was integrated into the German 1st Panzerdivision (= 1st Tank Division), in return for which German Panzerbataillon 414 (= Tank Battalion 414) was repositioned in Bergen and placed under the command of the said brigade. The battalion is mainly composed of German personnel and material, but one company consists of Dutch soldiers. The Netherlands will provide 16 Leopard 2 A6MA2 for this unit, which will be equipped with the A7 variant and officially become part of the German vehicle pool. In total, the Dutch tank company will be equipped with 18 battle tanks (= 16 Dutch vehicles plus two tanks from the German inventory). The German Bundeswehr will convert a further 18 Leopard 2 A6M to the A6MA2 variant and assign them to Panzerbataillon 414. It will make the tanks of this unit the first Leopard 2 of the Bundeswehr to be equipped with digital radio systems. Meanwhile, the German Army and the Dutch Koninklijke Landmacht (= Royal Army) cooperate in developing a new digital command system.

In 2018, the first Leopard 2 A6MA2s were handed over to Tank Battalion 414.

Between 1987 and 1993, **Switzerland** procured a total of 380 Leopard 2 A4s for its army. The Swiss designation is Panzer 87 Leopard. The majority of the Swiss Leos were produced under license in Switzerland. A public debate accompanied the procurement on the usefulness of battle tanks for a purely defensive army. Modifications compared to the German variants include installing U.S. radios including intercom systems and outside phones, additional snow-seizing tools, MG 87s as secondary armament, a modified NBC protection system, and the installation of exhaust silencers; in addition, further detailed modifications were carried out. Later, some tanks were further modified. Among other things, an adjustment system was retrofitted, the ammunition hatch was welded (where available), and heavy chain guards were installed. Under the 2006 Rüstungsprogramm 06, the active Leo fleet was shrunk to 134 tanks; these were equipped with modern command and control systems, a reversing aid, and further detailed improvements to ensure an ongoing supply, to be able to function as the backbone of the Swiss tank force at least until after the year 2025. 42 panzers were sold to Rheinmetall, the rest decommissioned.

The **Swedish Armed Forces** have two Leopard 2 variants under the designation Strv 121 and Strv 122 in its inventory. 160 Leopard 2 A4s were initially delivered to the troops as Strv 121 from January 1996 after the contract was signed in 1994. They were equipped with modified radios and other detailed modifications. At least 100 of these tanks were returned to Rheinmetall from 2014 onwards after being taken out of active service.

The first of a total of 120 Strv 122s reached Sweden in October 1995. Production was gradually transferred to Sweden, where the last vehicle rolled off the assembly line in 2001. The Strv 122 is a modified Leopard 2 A5. The modifications include additional (partly modular) armor plates on the commander's periscope, on the front hull and turret including an extended turret rear, modified liners for the entire fighting compartment, a digital command system called TCCS with touch screen (was later supplemented with GPS), an improved fire control computer including a new main periscope, French-made smoke mortars, an outside phone, a different navigation system, and a suction ventilation system for the engine compartment along with other detailed changes. It increases the combat weight to 62.5 tons. The TCCS allows numerous military vehicles of different models to be digitally connected, making it much easier to command a formation in combat. Saab's special thermal mat systems (designation: Barracuda) reduce the infrared and heat radiation of the tanks. The system comes with a parasol on the turret, which heightens the silhouette of the tank. Ten Leos were equipped with mine protection and designated as Strv 122B. They reach a combat weight of 65 tons.

It is planned to have 88 Strv 122 modernized by Krauss-Maffei Wegmann by 2023, including installing a battle management system and the replacement of obsolete components.

Spain initially took over 108 Leopard 2 A4s from the German Armed Forces in the mid-1990s (as Leopard 2 A4 E). These were modified with other radios. In 2004, the first of 219 newly produced vehicles with the designation Leopardo 2 E was handed over to the Spanish troops. This model's level of equipment corresponds to the Leopard 2 A6 variant with additional armoring on the turret, front hull, and side skirts, a digital command system called BMS similar to the Swedish one, the latest thermal imaging devices for commander and gunner, other radio equipment including an intercom and outside phone, air conditioning and an auxiliary power unit. The Modello 55-MG is the secondary armament in all Spanish vehicles. In 2018, the Spanish Armed Forces announced that the fire control computers of six Leopardo 2 Es would be modernized before the tanks would be placed under the command of the NATO battle group in Latvia.

Denmark purchased a total of 51 Leopard 2 A4s (as Leopard 2 A4 DK) from German Army stocks in 1997. The radios were changed to Danish standard radio systems. From 2002 on, all tanks were upgraded and designated Leopard 2 A5 DK, i.e., they were upgraded to the 2 A5 variant level and then further modified: the front hull armor was enhanced, additional snow-seizing tools were affixed, and one more searchlight was installed. An air conditioning system was also added to the turret, and a power supply unit was mounted. The turret rear was extended, a new smoke mortar system mounted, and further detail improvements were made. Instead, the anti-aircraft machine gun was dispensed. Later new weight-saving tracks were introduced.

To replace the Leopard 1 completely, another 18 Leopard 2 A4s were procured, and six of them converted to A5 DK. For foreign missions in hot regions, at least 14 vehicles were equipped with the following modifications and numerous changes to details: Barracuda thermal matting systems, wire deflectors on the turret roof, beige-green-brown camouflage paint job, additional armor plates, a compressor with a compressed air hose for cleaning the air filters, thermal imaging at the front and rear as aids for the driver, cooling vests for the crew, a tow shear, additional radio equipment, an improved fire extinguishing system and later extra mine protection components. For the Afghanistan mission, slat armor elements (cage amour, which is primarily intended to protect against shaped charges) were installed in some cases, and the anti-aircraft machine gun was re-equipped, or a 12.7-millimeter Browning machine gun was installed instead.

In 2016, the Danish government approved the Danish battle tank fleet's conversion to the A7 upgrade level. A report from 2014 says that the new ATTICA thermal imaging device is to be installed in the gunner's periscope. This indicates a certain harmonization attempt with the A7V upgrade package. Modernizing all Danish Leos should be completed by 2023. According to Ingvorsen (2018), Denmark will then have 44 active Leopard 2 A7s. Reducing its tank fleet to a total of 34 MBTs announced by Frank Lobitz in 2009 (Lobitz, F., 2009, p. 153) has thus not taken place, although Antonsen, in his publication from 2016, speaks about only 32 Leos in Denmark's service.

Between 1998 and 2001, **Austria** procured a total of 114 Leopard 2 A4s tanks from Dutch stocks (designation: Leopard 2 A4 Ö). New radios, a fire suppression system, and a digital smoke mortar system were gradually installed compared to the NL variant. In 2006, the active tank force was reduced to 56 Leopard 2 main battle tanks, for which a considerable need for investment in maintenance and modernization has now been identified, but apparently not yet remedied (Seidl, C., 2018). Nevertheless, the Austrian tank force is trained well and was thus able to win the Tank Challenge 2017 in Grafenwöhr, among others.

Norway also took advantage of the reduction of the Dutch tank force and went on a shopping spree. In 2001, a contract was signed to purchase 52 Leopard 2 A4 NLs, and delivery began the same year. The Norwegian Armed Forces had the German Army's smoke mortar system mounted back again on their Leopards, the installed radios were also replaced, and a battle management system introduced. Further modifications were made in detail, but the secondary armament of Belgian design was retained. In some cases, the lighter track coverings of the Leo 1 are used.

Since the end of the 2000s, there have been considerations to modernize Norway's main battle tank fleet or strengthen it by purchasing more modern Leopards. Various plans were repeatedly put on the table and then not implemented. Oslo is currently planning to modernize its main battle tanks only between 2025 and 2028.

In 2003, **Finland** received a total of 124 Leopard 2 A4s from old Bundeswehr stocks, 100 of which are intended for use as active battle tanks (under the designation Leopard 2 A4 FIN). The rest was converted to special tanks or is used as spare parts donors. In the following years, another 15 Leopard 2 A4s were purchased. Modifications were only made in detail; among other things, more snow-seizing tools were added, other radios were installed, and additional storage space was brought off. In 2014, Finland decided to modernize its tank force by purchasing 100 Dutch Leopard 2 A6s. The last of them were delivered in October 2019.

Poland procured 128 Leopard 2 A4s from Bundeswehr stocks for the first time in 2002, without modifying them in any way. They are designated as Leopard 2 A4 PL. Between May 2014 and December 2015, an additional 105 Leopard 2 A5s were delivered to the Polish Armed Forces and 14 further Leopard 2 vehicles of an unknown variant. In 2016, Rheinmetall announced that it would be upgrading the 128 Polish Leopard 2 A4 tanks to A5 respectively A6 on behalf of the Polish Army. Since the Polish and German tank forces work closely together, the Polish side is keen to keep its Leopard 2 fleet close to the German standard. In 2020 Gerhard Heiming even spoke of 142 Polish tanks to be retrofitted, which suits the 14 vehicles purchased subsequently. The modernization is being delayed because Warsaw is not satisfied with the quality of the prototype. The Polish Armed Forces' total of 247 Leopard 2s accounts for around 30 percent of Poland's main battle tank fleet, which also consists of Soviet T-72s and Polish PT-91s (upgraded T-72s).

Greece decided to purchase Leopard 2 battle tanks in 2002. Starting in 2005, an initial 183 Leopard 2 A4s were delivered from Bundeswehr stocks. The designation is Leopard 2 A4 GR. No significant changes were made. Besides, Greece procured 170 factory-fresh Leopard 2 HEL, a special variant based on an upgrade package similar to the Strv 122 variant. A Greek command support system was installed, as well as air conditioning, a crosswind sensor, and 2nd generation thermal imaging devices. Most vehicles were manufactured under license in Greece until 2009, with one batch of 30 tanks in Germany. After delivery, reports of unpaid invoices, defects in the delivered vehicles, and suspected bribery payments connected with the Leo 2 deal became known in public.

With signing the contract in 2005, **Turkey** also initially purchased 298 Leopard 2 A4s from German Army stocks (as Leopard 2 A4 TU). A little later, another 50 main battle tanks of the same variant were added to the order, which was not significantly modified. However, there are many indications that Turkish corporation Aselsan upgrades the Leos of the Turkish Army, among other things, by installing a modern fire control system. Improved air filters are also said to have been implemented. Also, there are reports of a so-called Next Generation upgrade by Aselsan. Photos clearly show additional armor plates on the turret and hull, making the tank look similar to a Leopard 2 A5. However, it remains unclear whether those modernization measures were carried out on the Turkish Leopard fleet beyond a prototype's production. The available photos of Leopard 2 tanks in northern Syria do not indicate that the additional armor from the Next Generation project has been mounted.

On the other hand, the Leopards deployed in the course of Operation Olive Branch in northern Syria may have been retrofitted with reactive armor and missile defense systems from Aselan (Kramper, G., 2018). In January 2018, Germany refused to equip Turkish Leopards with mine protection components in the wake of the recent Turkish offensive in northern Syria. According to reports from May 2020, it is now planned to have the first 84 Leopards, and later the entire Turkish Leo 2 fleet upgraded by the Turkish company BMC.

In November 2007, **Chile** concluded an agreement with the Federal Republic of Germany on the procurement of Leopard 2 A4s from old German stocks (Chilean designation: Leopard 2 A4 CHL). In response to a Kleine Anfrage (= inquiry by parliamentary groups in the Bundestag) from federal parliament delegates in 2013, the German government itself stated that 172 Leopard 2s had been delivered, not all of which were to be used as active main battle tanks. The Chilean Leopards were altered by installing an alternative radio system. The turret rear was also modified, and possibly a command system and GPS were fitted. Also, modifications were made to the engine to make it suitable for use in higher altitudes.

It has been agreed not to disclose the quantity of Leopard 2 A4s that **Singapore** purchased from stocks of the German Armed Forces in 2006. Reports from both states to the United Nations Register of Conventional Arms (UNROCA) suggest that between 160 and 165 tanks were delivered. However, it is assumed that some vehicles are intended to be used as special tanks or spare parts donors. The tanks are designated as Leopard 2 A4 SGP. Regarding the armament, it can be said that the Singaporean tanks were probably equipped with Belgian secondary armament, new radio systems, new smoke mortars, and (at least partially) with an auxiliary power unit. For the years 2016 to 2019, Germany notified the UN of the export of a further 45 Leopard 2s to Singapore. Still, it did not specify whether the delivery was completed and which variants were to be delivered. In addition, the arms register reports often summarize all vehicles based on the Leopard 2 chassis, including armored vehicle-launched bridges and the like. Singapore only confirmed that it had purchased 96 Leopard 2 A4s in 2006, 66 of which were integrated into the active tank fleet. Singapore denies a further purchase of Leopards, and the German government has classified information about arms deliveries to Singapore as confidential. However, there are reports that Krauss-Maffei Wegmann is manufacturing brand new Leopard 2 A7s for Singapore – these reports could refer to the second delivery, which began in 2016. Meanwhile, there are increasing indications that Singapore has further modified some or all her Leos: Additional armor plates in the form of slat armoring as well as MEXAS composite armor, developed by the company Deisenroth, were at least mounted on the turret and side skirts. In 2009 this upgrade measure only could be suspected by Frank Lobitz. Now it seems to be confirmed by an article by Mike Yeo in DefenseNews and the corresponding photo. Finally, without access to insider knowledge, one can only speculate on how many Leopard 2 main battle tanks of which variants the Singaporean Armed Forces have at their disposal.

Portugal took over 37 Leopard 2 A6s from the Netherlands between 2008 and 2009 (as Leopard 2 A6 PRT). Digital radio equipment and a battle management system were retrofitted. A modernization of the tank fleet is planned for the period 2026 to 2030. According to the description of the planned modifications, it seems to be an upgrade to the A7V variant.

In 2007, **Canada** decided in the urgent search for an interim solution to procure the Leopard 2. At the time, Ottawa needed a tank that was promptly available for operations in Afghanistan under ISAF mandate, offered outstanding mine protection, and could build a bridge between the Leopard 1, which was about to be finally phased out, and a new type of main battle tank to be procured from 2030. "Promptly" is indeed the magic word in this case because Canada wanted to deploy the tanks ASAP in Afghanistan. 20 Leopard 2 A6Ms were leased from Berlin in a rush (as Leopard 2 A6M CAN). Since the Federal Republic of Germany did not have enough 2 A6Ms in store, some vehicles were taken from the active tank force of the German Heer for export to Canada. A record-breaking five months elapsed between the signing of the Leopards' procurement contract and delivery. Only a short time later, the Leos were already engaged in combat operations at the Hindu Kush.

The 2 A6Ms were modified as follows: Installing Canadian standard radio equipment, additional front hull armor plate, cooling scoop, and additional storage boxes. The MG3 was initially retained as secondary armament for time reasons. In Afghanistan, some crews exchanged the anti-aircraft machine gun for the Belgian 7.62-millimeter C6 GPMG, which was also used in the Leopard 1 C2 and could be mounted on the turret of the Leo 2 without any problems. Additional slat armor elements were mounted on the side and rear for ISAF operations to increase protection against RPG fire. Also, a counter IED jammer was installed – that is a device that suppresses close range mobile radio frequencies to prevent explosives from being detonated via remote control. Further detailed changes were made over time; for example, the Barracuda thermal matting system, including a parasol on the roof, was introduced in April 2008. An air conditioning system may also have already been retrofitted in Afghanistan.

Later, Canada procured 100 Leopard 2 battle tanks from Dutch stocks (20 Leopard 2 A6 NLs and 80 2 A4 NLs), 15 additional Leo 2 A4s from Germany as spare parts donors, and 12 tanks from Switzerland, which were converted into special tanks. In 2009, the Canadian government announced its intention to procure 29 mine plows, mine rollers, and dozer blades for the Canadian Army's Leo 2 fleet as part of an upgrade program. Initial tests were carried out in the same year with a Leopard 2 A6M CAN before at least mine rollers were used in combat situations. These mine rollers are used pre-stressed. This way, they rumble across the ground in front of the tank and thus trigger mines and IEDs.

The first 20 Leopard 2 A4 CANs (or 2 A4M CAN; Lobitz calls this variant 2 A4(Ops) CAN) from the deal with the Netherlands were handed over to the troops in October 2010. The last followed in the first half of 2011. Prior they had been retrofitted by Krauss-Maffei Wegmann in order to meet the demands of the Canadian Army. The modifications include mine protection from the A6M upgrade package, additional armor plates on the hull sides and turret, slat armor elements, spall liners in the fighting compartment, and special seats for the driver and commander as well as improved suspension, thus significantly increasing the protection factor. Besides, a digital electronic system including new controls and a digitalized electronic turret drive was installed, as well as a counter IED jammer. Furthermore, a front and rear camera with night vision capability (residual light amplifier plus thermal image) for the driver, Canadian radio systems, and another secondary armament (C6 GPMG) were introduced. Operating mine plows and similar extensions were prepared. Barracuda thermal mats were also procured for the A4M and cooling vests for the crews. The Leo 2 A4 CAN reaches a combat weight of 61.8 tons and is optimized for asymmetric warfare imposed on the Canadian Armed Forces in Afghanistan. In contrast, the Leo 2 A6M CAN is optimized for tank versus tank duel situations.

In 2014 it was announced that more than 100 Canadian Leopard 2s would be retrofitted with new thermal imaging devices for the commander and gunner.

As compensation for the 20 leased tanks, Canada later sent the 20 A6 NLs converted to A6Ms back to Germany. In this way, the initially leased tanks could remain in Afghanistan. In total, the Canadian Armed Forces have 20 A6Ms and 20 A4Ms available for operations, while 42 Leopard 2 A4s serve as tanks for training purposes. The rest of the vehicles procured are used as spare parts donors or as platforms for special tanks. The Canadian Armed Forces now plan with their Leo fleet until around 2035. In 2019, further upgrades were considered, which would lead to an A8 upgrade level, which is currently under development. This measure could extend the Leopards' service life until 2050.

Indonesia signed a contract in 2012 for the purchase of 103 modified Leopard 2 A4s from Bundeswehr stocks. The tanks were delivered until the end of 2016. Before this, Rheinmetall modified them to the extent that they were made suitable for deployments in the tropical climate zone. They are designated Leopard 2 A4 IR.

Between 2015 and 2018, Krauss-Maffei Wegmann delivered 62 Leopard 2 A7+s to the **State of Qatar**.

In 2018, **Hungary** ordered 44 brand-new Leopard 2 A7+s and 12 Leopard 2 A4s from old Bundeswehr stocks. Delivery began in July 2020 with the handover of four A4 vehicles.

References for this Chapter

For the total number of Leopard 2s in the German Armed Forces, compare Hilmes (2006) and Spielberger (1995) for further details on the first four construction batches. Zwilling (2018a) and (2018b) refer to the use of Leopards in the Bundeswehr and even speak of 328 planned Leopard 2s in the future, as does Kohl (2019). For the officially announced size of Germany's future tank fleet from 2025 on, see Ulbrich (2019). Supplementary also Schulze (2020). Frank Lobitz's publication from 2009 offers rich information on most user countries. For Hungary, see Mitteldeutscher Rundfunk (2020) and Heiming (2018). Indonesia's arms deal can be found in NurW (2016) and Rheinmetall Defence (2013). Leo 2 deals with Poland and Qatar are discussed by Lühr Henken (undated). Additionally, compare Zwilling (2018b), Hamburger Abendblatt (2013), UNROCA (2020), Heiming (2020), and Rheinmetall Group (2016) on Poland. For the recent developments in the Dutch Army, see Die Presse (2011), Wiegold (2015b), Wiegold (2016a), Wiegold (2019), and Twigt (2018). The Swiss Leopard fleet development can be traced in Der Bundesrat (2006) and (2010). Detailed information on the procurement of the original Leopard 2 batches by the Swiss and the Netherlands can be found in Krapke (1984). For the Strv 121, see Nasr (2014) and Max (2016). Spain's latest modernization measures can be read about in 21st Century Asian Arms Race (2018). For further information on Denmark, see also Dan (2019), Schulze (2011), Antonsen (2016), and Ingvorsen (2018). Note: Thomas Antonsen is mistaken in his book's introduction since he states that Canada sent her Leopard 1 tanks on operations in Afghanistan in 2005. The current state of the Austrian Leos is outlined by Seidl (2018). The more recent development of the Norwegian tank force is discussed in Wiegold (2015a) and Max (2018). For Finland, see Shephard (2019). The crudities surrounding the Leo 2 deal with Greece is treated in Bockenheimer & Simantke (2015). Turkey's additional deal of 50 Leos, not listed by Lobitz, is addressed in the German government's response to a Kleine Anfrage in the Bundestag (2013). For Turkey's modernization efforts, see Aziz (2017), Malyasov (2015), Railly News

(2020), Mister Análisi (2017), Kramper (2018), and Defence Turkey (2011). Germany's denial of retrofitting Turkish panzers with additional mine protection is discussed in Frankfurter Allgemeine (2018). HNA (2016) and Yeo (2019) provide information on Singapore. The UN arms register is a rich if often incomplete source for international tank deliveries: UNROCA (undated). For Portugal, see the post of theoderich (2019) with a compilation of relevant sources. Facts about Canada's tank force can be found in Defense Industry Daily (2014), Krauss-Maffei Wegmann (undated, d), Schulze (2010a) and (2015), and Allan Joyner (2019), which also mentions the ATTICA thermal imaging devices for Danish Leopard 2s. Defense Industry Daily states that the Leopard 2 A6M CAN has been retrofitted with air conditioning in Afghanistan, while Frank Lobitz and Carl Schulze explicitly mention the lack of air conditioning. Several photos of A4Ms in Afghanistan clearly show that the crews continue to wear cooling vests.

Combat History

Leo 2s in Bosnia

Since the UN blue helmets deployed within UNPROFOR mission were not taken seriously by the conflict parties, and Dutch soldiers allowed the massacre of Srebrenica, among other things, to happen, the Armed Forces of the Netherlands relied on the factor of deterrence for the follow-up missions IFOR and SFOR. Therefore they sent heavy equipment to Bosnia, and this means Leopard 2 tanks. They should remain a deterrent for both missions since the tanks did not get into a combat situation.

For IFOR, the Dutch Koninklijke Landmacht relied on Leopard 2 A4 tanks and crews from 1st Tankbataljon. The troops were transported by ship to Split and unloaded there in January 1996.

For SFOR, The Hague transferred Leopard 2 A5s to Bosnia to support Operation Joint Guard.

The tanks were specially retrofitted with a so-called Motorola box for the Balkan mission, which made radioing in Bosnia's rugged karst landscape possible. It is unclear whether Dutch tanks were still part of the follow-up mission Operation Joint Forge after June 1998.

Leopards conquer Kosovo

From June 12, 1999, NATO troops invaded Kosovo under KFOR mandate (Operation Joint Guardian). About 6,000 German soldiers participated in the invasion. The Bundeswehr had set up a reinforced mechanized battalion (vstk MechBtl) for this purpose, which had been equipped with personnel and material from 37 different units. Among others, the spearhead was made up of armored forces of the Panzerbrigade 21 Lipperland; these were provided by the 4th company of Panzerbataillon 33 from Luttmersen as well as by the 3rd company of Panzerbatallion 214 from Augustdorf. They were equipped, among other things, with Leopard 2 A5 battle tanks. They shaped the following units within vstk MechBtl: 3/214 formed 2nd Einsatzkompanie (= deployment company) with Panzerzug (= armored platoon) A, B, C, and D; the 4/33 formed 4th Einsatzkompanie, also consisting of Panzerzug A to D. According to Rolf Clemens, Defence Minister Rudolf Scharping decided to use main battle tanks for the KFOR mission because of the experience the Danes had gained with their Leopards in Bosnia. When the public learned about this, a debate broke out about whether tanks were the right instruments for a peace mission.

A total of 28 German Leo 2 A5s were used in the invasion of Kosovo. Then again, a number of 33 involved Leopard 2s circulates among some sources too, for example on the website of the former member of the Bundestag for Bündnis 90/Die Grünen (= Greens), Winfried Nachtwei, as well as in the vstk MechBtl structure overview, which can be found in Maximilian Eder's book. At least Nachtwei's contribution can be exposed as poorly researched, since he speaks, among other things, of the deployment of Dutch Panzerhaubitze 2000s in June 1999. However, the Dutch did not procure this weapon system until later. On the other hand, Eder makes it clear that the overview includes reserves, which could explain the five additional tanks. It may also concern special tanks on the Leopard platform.

The invasion of the German tanks was carried out in combination with Panzergrenadiers (= German mechanized infantry) and other troops, which rolled in long columns over Macedonian, Albanian, and Kosovar roads. It presented a novel picture, especially for the German public. Only months after Germany's participation in the NATO air war against Serbia without any UN mandate whatsoever had been controversially discussed, the NATO invasion now seemed to confirm the fears of those who had warned against new militarism. On the other hand, a little more than 20 years later, against the background of the development of Kosovo and the entire region ever after, the whole KFOR mission can also be viewed favorably. With the invasion of Kosovo, the Bundeswehr sent its Leo 2s on possible combat operations for the first time. Almost 20 years early, the first Leopard 2 had been handed over to the German troops.

But one after the other: With the order of February 1, 1999, the Heeresführungskommando (= Army Forces Command) initially instructed to set up that mentioned above reinforced mechanized battalion along with other units for the upcoming task. After a brief restructuring phase, the two nominated tank companies underwent preliminary operational training until the end of March, focusing on the extraction of OSCE observers, who were still in Kosovo at the time, before an agonizing period of waiting began. For a long time, it remained unclear whether, and if so, when, they would be transferred to the Balkans. In addition to a possible invasion of Kosovo (back then, NATO airstrikes continued with an uncertain outcome), at times, German participation in Operation Joint Guarantor Tier 3 was considered – an operation, which ultimately did not have to be carried out.

Since the end of February, the vstk MechBtl's large equipment and accompanying personnel have been transferred by sea to Thessaloniki. The Greek side did not always show itself to be cooperative, which is evident in Werner Pfeil's memoir "Ein Sommertag im Krieg" (2019) as well as in Sean Maloney's publication (2019). In part under unworthy conditions, NATO soldiers were accommodated on Greek soil; violent demonstrators and a generally hostile attitude toward foreign troops were omnipresent.

From Thessaloniki, the large equipment was transferred by land to Krivolak in Macedonia. There a field maintenance station and military training area were hastily built. The decision in favor of Krivolak meant that equipment and crews were housed separately, which made technical service of the equipment more difficult. In an article in Eder's book, the then Major Radig, in particular, points out this circumstance as problematic. And Werner Pfeil speaks of the "largest storage area for large equipment" (Pfeil, W., 2019, p. 90, own translation). Some vehicles and tanks stood motionless in Krivolak for so long that green shoots sprouted from the barrels, and damages occurred.

The Macedonian barracks Kuzman Josifovski Pitu in Tetovo, about 150 kilometers away, served as one of the main bases for the German KFOR contingent personnel. Besides, a large camp was built outside the city (Camp Erebino on the mountain of the same name). The hostile atmosphere in Greece was later also felt by the rest of the personnel selected for the invasion. Between May and early June 1999, they were transferred by plane to Thessaloniki, where they continued to Tetovo. The OSCE observers had already left Kosovo at that time.

In the darkness, the Bw soldiers in Tetovo and the Erebino camp could hear NATO aircrafts bombing Kosovo and Serbia. A flickering glow of flames across the border and the position lights in the starry sky dominated many a night.

Werner Pfeil vividly describes the tense situation that the Bundeswehr soldiers had to endure in Macedonia; in addition to the noise of the war coming over from the neighboring country, thousands of refugees had to be taken care of. Also, the German soldiers had to come to terms with a population that was increasingly hostile to NATO troops. German Army vehicles commuting between the locations in Macedonia were sometimes thrown stones at them.

The war caught up with the German Leopard crews in Camp Erebino before they set foot in Kosovo. Once, they were startled by a radio message in the weeks before the invasion: Serbian MiG-29 fighter aircraft are on their way! The German Armed Forces troops hastily cleared the Erebino and loaded their anti-aircraft weapons, but a Serbian airstrike did not occur. Another incident occurred sometime later: artillery fire struck along the border on Macedonian soil, including in the immediate vicinity of the positions of German security forces for the camp. Foreign armored vehicles finally approached the Germans, and infantrymen dismounted. It was not until the following day that it was discovered that this had been an unannounced exercise by the Macedonian Army. Pfeil's report shows how much such encounters affected the author's mood; after all, NATO was expecting a Serbian attack at any time.

Large parts of the personnel moved to Krivolak in the course of May 1999 to prepare their vehicles for the forthcoming invasion. They transferred them to Tetovo or Petrovec near Skopje between the end of May and the beginning of June. The 2nd Company reported combat readiness in Tetovo already on May 29, the 4th company followed on June 7 in Petrovec. In the following days, the vstk MechBtl pulled together its units there, some of which did not even have time to properly check their equipment. For example, the vehicles' KFOR labels had to be improvised; pizza boxes cut out into letters served as templates. The soldiers prepared themselves for the fact that they would be deployed without much lead time. The last restructuring measures were carried out hastily, including the reintegration of two 2nd Company tank platoons (B and C) into the battalion. Previously they had been attached to those formations invading Kosovo over Albania, but the route over Albania was finally considered impassable for main battle tanks.

On June 11, combat loads were issued, and readiness for action was established. Hauptmann Kirchhoff writes in his contribution to the new edition of Eder's publication about the first KFOR rotation (as the author already standing in the rank of an Oberstleutnant i. G.) that this was probably the first time for many German tank soldiers to hold the black live ammunition of the Leopard 2 in their hands. After orders were issued at 21:00 hrs, Oberstleutnant Eder addressed his battalion. Most of those involved must have been aware that a historic moment was imminent. The last time German soldiers had set foot on Kosovar soil, they had worn Wehrmacht or Waffen SS uniforms.

In the morning of June 12, 1999 (hours vary between 10:00 and 12:45 hrs, depending on the source), the troops were instructed to gather. At the same time, the Advance Party of the Bundeswehr (2nd Company) – a reinforced mechanized company with a total of 34 tracked and large vehicles, including six Leopard 2 A5s, and about 200 soldiers under the leadership of deputy battalion commander, Major Burchardi – started moving towards the Macedonian-Kosovarian border as part of a large NATO column (British 2nd Dragoons Royal Scots Greys and Royal Gurkha Rifles as well as a Canadian mechanized recce company of Lord Strathcona's Horse). In addition to the main battle tanks and Panzergrenadiers with their Marder infantry fighting vehicles, the Advance Party consisted of a mixed Jäger (= German light infantry) platoon on APC Fuchs' and Luchs reconnaissance armored fighting vehicles, a light anti-aircraft platoon equipped with Stinger, a Dutch air control team, a mobile medical team, medics, a supply unit, a reconnaissance liaison group and a team of German elite special forces (KSK).

Canadian Captain Chris Hunt of the Strathcona's was impressed by the firepower NATO had assembled for Kosovo's invasion. Mechanized forces from different nations marched in while Apache helicopters dominated the airspace.

The initial goal was to occupy the area of operations in Prizren with the aforementioned Advance Party over the so-called Eastern Route. With the Eastern Route, the route Skopje-Prizren was meant. Eight tunnels and 16 bridges had to be crossed, which the Leopard 2, in particular, could only pass one at a time due to its high combat weight. Also, broken-down vehicles of the Yugoslavian Army, which had simply been abandoned on the retreat, repeatedly hindered the advance. The unclear mine situation led to delays, even though the British and U.S. Americans had cleared the main marching routes quickly. Away from the main roads, however, uncertainty lurked.

The Advance Party reached the border crossing with a Leo 2 A5 and a Marder as its vanguard around noon. There Kosovar refugees awaited them and cheered frenetically. Previously, other NATO units had already entered Kosovo from 05:00 hrs, including British paratroopers and Gurkhas. They had secured border crossings and assisted in mine clearance. After crossing the border, the Advance Party moved through the narrowness of Kaçanik towards Prizren, a town in the southern tip of the country.

About 30 kilometers beyond the border, the German Advance Party separated from the remaining NATO forces and continued the march on its own. Then the clouds opened up, and rain came down in buckets. Some radios failed, the British and Americans took a wrong turn and now blocked the way. The marching route's often unpaved roads became impassable, so that the Advance Party had to explore an alternative route at nightfall near Ferizaj.

First, the Advance Party came into contact with a Serbian colonel; later, it surprised a Serbian column with tanks and heavy guns near Stimlje. This encounter made it clear that a peaceful invasion of Kosovo was by no means set in stone and that the situation could escalate at any time: At first, the Serbian soldiers were startled, so they moved out of the way, but then drunken Serbs blocked the road. Suddenly Leopard 2s and Yugoslavian T-55s stood directly opposite each other. They were so close that the tank commanders could almost shake hands, as Stabsfeldwebel Flender later reported. The Serbs sent the German invaders hostile looks and made middle finger gestures. Nevertheless, an outbreak of violence did not occur. The Bundeswehr troops even supplied the Serbs with fuel and escorted them a part of the way.

In the Stimlje Pass, the Advance Party was fired at for the first time. Bullets flew far too high over the German vehicles. It remained unclear who had opened fire. In Suva Reka, the Bw column encountered celebrating UÇK fighters.

The Advance Party finally reached Prizren around midnight after crossing the Dulje Pass. When German military vehicles invaded the town, they were quickly surrounded by cheering people. In their celebratory mood, civilians climbed the turret of a Leopard 2 and danced on it under thunderous "NATO!" shouts. (In his memoirs, Major Radig is the only one to report on a deserted city upon the arrival of the Advance Party – but videos and other sources support the story of a cheering crowd dancing on tanks). When the Germans met Yugoslavian soldiers, there were sometimes heated arguments before the Yugoslavs retreated, but there were also friendly encounters. War ruins dominated the townscape of Prizren. It was unclear how the various (and in part armed) parties in the country would react to the NATO invasion. Hence, the situation on those June days was tense, and the Bundeswehr soldiers, who took part in the first major German foreign deployment since the end of the war, had to be prepared for anything. In addition to the various conflicting parties, mines and unexploded ordnances were an omnipresent danger. Fighters of the UÇK, soldiers of the Yugoslavian Army, and men of Serbian special police units were still on site. The situation was highly explosive. At the same time, the majority of the population showed great sympathy for the arriving soldiers. Leopard tanks were decorated with flowers by enthusiastic bystanders. Soldiers were lifted and carried by the exuberant crowd.

Additional troops of the German Armed Forces marched into Kosovo from Albania on the morning of June 13. At the Morinë border crossing, contrary to the agreement, they still met soldiers of the Yugoslavian People's Army. They had to form a buffer between them and the refugees streaming into Kosovo. This is also the place where the legendary episode of Brigadegeneral Helmut Harff originated, who issued a clear ultimatum to the Yugoslav officers in front of several TV cameras: "You have to leave within 30 minutes! (...) That is the end of discussion! You have now 28 minutes!" On the other side of the border, Harff's units were welcomed by Leopard 2s of 2nd Einsatzkompanie under the command of Company Commander Hauptmann Stephan Kirchhoff. One tank joined the vanguard of the invading troops, and the rest later accompanied the main column. Thus, the majority of the Bundeswehr's forces were secured by Leopard 2 A5s while marching into Kosovo. On the way to Prizren, German battle tanks once again met, among others, Yugoslavian T-55s on their withdrawal to Serbia. Werner Pfeil, who was part of that very vanguard, reports in this context of an explosion that occurred about 500 meters to the side of the column led by a Leo 2. Debris rained on the road, but the origin or cause of the explosion could not be determined first. Only later did it turn out that an armored personnel carrier of the retreating Yugoslav Armed Forces had probably hit a mine. Mine warning signs could be seen everywhere, and burnt-out ruins, vehicles, corpses, animal carcasses, and shot down tanks lined the marching route. The German Armed Forces also passed illegal UÇK checkpoints on their way into the city.

Meanwhile, other Leopard tanks of the Advance Party had taken up position on the western edge of Prizren with camouflage nets thrown over them. They were assigned to prevent Serbian forces from entering the city. They received the vanguard of the Western Route coming from Albania. Once again, with the Leo 2 taking the lead, German troops entering the city could only make their way through the cheering crowd at a walking pace. A young woman fearlessly scaled the Leopard 2 of the vanguard, kissed the commander looking out of the hatch on both cheeks, and presented him with flowers.

On the same day, Leo tanks and German Feldjäger (= military policemen) and light infantrymen from the Western Route vanguard were assigned escorting Serbian troops stuck between the Albanian border and Prizren. Their target area was the British sector. The operation went off without any incident, and the Serbs, hated by many residents and the UÇK, were able to leave the area unharmed.

Other Leopard 2s of the Advance Party were reassigned to Suva Reka. Again they had to make their way through a cheering sea of people. Meanwhile, retreating units of the Yugoslav Army and Serbian special police were threatened, and some men were even beaten, so that warning shots were fired over and over again in Prizren. The situation was chaotic, and NATO had difficulty gaining a clear picture.

The climax of the agitated situation on June 13, 1999, was an incident in Prizren, where the crew of a Leopard 2 A5 of A Platoon/2nd Company and some German soldiers on foot was threatened and obviously attacked by two Serbian paramilitaries. In the evening of that day, a yellow Lada raced towards a German checkpoint in the middle of the city near the Fuchs Bridge, where the tank, as mentioned earlier, was positioned.

"This is Alpha Two, one car, yellow Lada, just broke through the barrier! We identified two armed persons in the car," the radio operator of an APC Fuchs reported at the end of the town. (I translated the radio message from German).

The driver held a hand grenade in his hand; the front-seat passenger fired a Kalashnikov, while the Lada zigzagged towards the checkpoint. The Leopard crew was not altogether on board, so the Leo did not intervene in the following firefight. The Germans soldiers on-site first loudly urged the men in Serbo-Croatian to stop, combined with the threat to shoot, as they had learned in training. Leutnant Ferk, who was the leader of the soldiers on foot, finally fired a warning shot. Thereupon an Oberfeldwebel was wounded in the arm by a ricochet. Thus Ferk ordered his men to open fire on the Lada. The vehicle stopped, then rolled backward. The German soldiers perforated the slowly backward rolling Lada with MG3s, pistol P8s, and G36s. Hits punched holes in the vehicle, shredded dimmed headlights and windows. A pool of oil quickly formed under the Lada. The driver died in a hail of bullets. Two civilians finally approached the vehicle and disarmed the badly wounded front-seat passenger, who was shortly afterward treated by German paramedics and transported away for medical treatment. He succumbed to his wounds two days later. Among the German soldiers were the tankers Leutnant and platoon leader Peter Vollmers and Stabsunteroffizier Martin Waltemathe. Waltemathe is visible in the video that exists of the incident. He lies behind the turret of the Leopard 2 A5 and fires his pistol at the Lada.

Staff sergeant Martin Waltemathe hides behind the turret of his Leopard 2 during the incident in Prizren and fires his pistol at the Lada

The Leopard 2 stands motionless at the roadside during the incident in Prizren

A total of around 220 shots were fired at the attackers. Ferk was honored by Rudolf Scharping for his actions with the Ehrenkreuz der Bundeswehr (= Badge of Honor) in gold. In the aftermath, however, criticism was also voiced about the German actions on that day; see, for example, Köhler, O., 2000, who states that the Lada was driven by drunkards rather than by irregular soldiers willing to kill. They even had tried to flee the first shots had been fired by the Bundeswehr soldiers but were nevertheless eliminated. For my taste, Köhler exaggerates his criticism when he compares the incident in Prizren with orders of the Wehrmacht for retaliatory actions against the Yugoslavian population from World War II. The Public Prosecution

Department in Koblenz later certified that the soldiers involved had not committed any breaches of the law.

In an interview, Vollmers assessed the incident as a positive signal to the Kosovar population. It showed everyone that the Germans were willing and able to carry out their mission by force. Werner Pfeil shares this view in his book.

German main battle tanks performed security duties around Prizren throughout June 13, 1999, and the night. 2nd Company was initially accommodated in a former tea factory on the southwest edge of the town. Later the whole vstk MechBtl was gathered and housed in the east of the town.

In the evening of June 13, around 18:00 hrs, the main forces of the Bundeswehr (remnants of the vstk MechBtl as well as support troops of the deployment brigade) from Albania and Skopje set off, including the remaining Leopard 2 A5s. The first marching unit (Eastern Route) consisted of 104 vehicles. Dutch artillerymen were also attached to the vstk MechBtl. The situation remained unclear. New clashes with firearms between Serbs and the UÇK were reported from Prizren.

The streets in Macedonia were lined with celebrating spectators, which sometimes allowed progress only at walking speed. During the night, the first marching unit crossed the border into Kosovo.

Two events that occurred during the night on the march over the Eastern Route to Prizren, which is linked in time, are exemplary of the exhausting tension that the men and women of KFOR had to endure between jubilation and horror: at around 03:30 hrs, the leading platoon near the Dulje Pass came across a corpse on the side of the road with a bullet in the head; a red car was parked near the road. The explosive ordnance disposal team, which was called upon and approached, found no evidence of booby traps but did find an identification document. The man in question was Volker Krämer, 56 years old, a German citizen, and one of two reporters from the Stern Magazine who had been murdered the day before. When the body was recovered, a loud bang occurred twice near the back third of the column. It was detonations, but its origin remained unclear. Nobody was hurt. Soon it turned out that the column had long been under the observation of UÇK fighters, but they were acting peacefully. News on the incident with the yellow Lada may also have recently reached the soldiers on the march. Along the way, the Germans once again encountered both an enthusiastic population and individual stone-throwers.

The Eastern Route column reached Prizren at dawn on June 14, and this time the streets were almost deserted (only Uffelmann speaks of people celebrating the arrival of the main forces – and Pfeil reports that the celebrating people in Prizren gathered in certain places, while other streets seemed to be deserted).

The first weeks in Prizren were a challenge due to the lack of infrastructure. The German tankers lived and slept partly on, in, or under their Leopards. Besides, KFOR had to take over police duties immediately after arrival, as public order collapsed with the withdrawal of the Serbs. But first of all, this very withdrawal had to be secured without violence because armed UÇK men were already streaming into the city from all sides. Even a main battle tank from Miloševićs troops was still in Prizren. Shots were fired again and again, but no battles emerged.

Leopard 2 tanks were used in quick reaction platoons and moved out several times to end inter-ethnic firefights. Mechanized forces of the 2nd Company also secured the border crossing into Albania. There was an equally chaotic situation, with up to 20,000 refugees returning daily to Kosovo – their homeland – despite the unclear mine situation. Checkpoints were established.

In his publication on the Canadian Operation Kinetic, Sean Maloney gives the army pilot Captain Aaron Nickerson his chance to speak. Nickerson describes an encounter between German, British, and U.S. main battle tanks with the UÇK and Yugoslav mechanized forces, including tanks in retreat. The incident is neither dated nor is a location given. Since Nickerson mentions German battle tanks for this specific encounter in a subordinate clause without further explanation, and since no German source can be found, German participation in this incident must be called into question. For the sake of completeness, I will discuss it anyway: Said Yugoslav mechanized column hid in a row of trees from British Challenger tanks that advanced across the road. Nickerson observed the situation from the air. The Challengers stopped and aimed their main armaments at the Yugoslav forces, urging them to continue their retreat. But then the hour of the UÇK came. Several fighters stormed over a hill towards the Yugoslav troops, firing RPGs. A battle between the two conflicting parties broke out. Only when German and U.S. tanks came into sight and approached did the UÇK withdraw again. As a result, a Lada raced toward a British Warrior tracked vehicle, and one of the Lada's occupants fired a Kalashnikov at it. The Warrior returned fire from his 30-millimeter cannon, scattering the Lada and its occupants throughout the surrounding area. I do not doubt that this episode happened that way, but I believe that no German tanks were involved – or at most at a distance where their crews were unaware of the incident.

After the invasion, the German tank soldiers experienced first-hand the rollercoaster ride of emotions that held the multi-ethnic population of Kosovo spellbound throughout the entire area of responsibility: the Kosovo Albanians were cheering German tanks and decorating them with flowers, and here the Serbs, who faced the Bundeswehr with skepticism or even rejection and who were perceptibly permeated with fear of reprisals by the Albanians.

Again and again, individual tanks or tank platoons were deployed in mixed units, for example, for a 4-week operation in Dragas south of Prizren, where the Bundeswehr soldiers proved themselves simultaneously as police, administration, and reconstruction experts. In addition, in the event of an attack by Serbian troops on Kosovo, the German tanks were considered in NATO's war plans for a counterattack in the Podujeva area north of Pristina with its three main roads. There they would have fought together with Canadian Leopard 1 C1s to secure the border.

On June 15, 1999, the 4th Company was ordered to march to Orahovac and therefore was put under the command of the Dutch 11th Self-propelled Artillery Battalion (Luitenant-kolonel van Loon). Two of the company's tank platoons remained in Prizren, however. The task of 4th Company in Orahovac showed the whole range of KFOR's mission: Operating a checkpoint north of the village, patrolling, providing a quick reaction platoon, guarding the village, especially the Serbian quarter and the Serbian mayor, and guarding a mass grave in Velica Krusa, which was filled with women, children, and men who had been shot and burned. The infrastructure in Orahovac and the bivouac area of the Germans was devastated. Until June 21, there was no electricity in the town. The soldiers slept again in and on their vehicles and had to build latrines for their nature's call. Before that, every square inch of land had to be searched for mines and UXOs (unexploded ordnances). Also, a constant danger emanated from the many unexploded ordnances that had been scattered in the area by cluster bombs as well as from uranium-enriched ammunition that had turned Serbian tank wrecks into radiating nuclear traps.

On June 23, 1999, German tank soldiers caught 30 civilians looting and arrested them.

An incident involving German Leopard 2 A5s occurred in late June 1999 in Orahovac (Frank Lobitz dates this incident to June 26, Joachim Lohse to June 28): At first, the cases of arson were frequent in the village, then there was also a shooting in the hospital. To nip any further escalation in the bud, van Loon decided to prepare two of his self-propelled howitzers to fire warning shots. In addition, Oberfeldwebel Olaf Hemann's Leopard 2 was to take up an elevated position outside the city. At night, when a patrol reported a fire and a crowd of people marching toward the hospital (in fact, they were UÇK men hurrying to the city's fire truck), the firing order was given to the tank howitzers and Hemann. The howitzers illuminated the city as bright as day with flare ammunition, and Hemann then opened fire from his 120-millimeter gun. The spectacle was repeated to amplify the effect. Hemann fired a total of four warning shots over the town. These were the first shots fired by a tank under the German flag since the end of the war as part of a real military mission. After this action, there were no more cases of arson in Orahovac for quite some time.

76

The Bundeswehr relied on its Leopard 2s as a show of force device by letting them patrol the AOR, especially at the beginning of the KFOR mission. Still, soon afterward, it abandoned using tracked vehicles for this purpose. Since then, the tanks remained mostly in their camps (initially in Prizren, but from 2000 on also in Suhareka). In order to deter Belgrade and demonstrate KFORS' strength to the residents of Kosovo, the Constant Resolve exercise was held in November 1999. In the course of this exercise, a Leopard 2 platoon (the Canadian source for this event speaks in the original text of a "Troop of Leopard 2s" (Maloney, S., 2019, Pos. 4136 in Kindle format)) probably moved to Podujevo together with other troops of the MNB (S).

The German Leo 2 A5s were replaced by Leopard 2 A4s between the end of 2000 and the beginning of 2001. The situation was now considered less dangerous, and the deployed 2 A5s were to be maintained and upgraded at home. Note that the assertion made in Zwilling's publication (2020) about the Leopard 2 A5s of the KFOR contingent being replaced by 2 A4s in August 2001 is probably a mistake. In fact, all other sources – including, by the way, Zwilling himself in his article on the Leo 2 A5 – speak in favor of the period from late 2000 to early 2001 being the time for replacing the tanks.

At the end of 2004, all German battle tanks were withdrawn from Kosovo.

Tetovo and Operation Essential Harvest

When Bundeswehr soldiers stationed in Tetovo, Macedonia, came under fire from the UÇK starting March 13, 2001, the leadership ordered Marder infantry fighting vehicles and Leopard 2 A4s to the scene of the incident, where they arrived on March 14. At that time, the third rotation of the German KFOR contingent was in the Balkans.

According to Defense Minister Rudolf Scharping, the tanks served to send an unmistakable warning to the rebels. In Macedonia, unlike in Kosovo, however, the German troops only had the right of self-defense. Against this background, the actual use of armaments of the Leopards against the UÇK appears extremely unlikely. There also is no evidence for this. Concerning the intermezzo in Tetovo, the literature does not always make a clear distinction between the Bundeswehr's reaction to the fighting in Tetovo on the one hand and the deployment in Macedonia as part of Operation Essential Harvest beginning in August 2001 on the other. In his publication on the development and deployment of the Leopard 2 A4, Ralph Zwilling, for example, says that this specific Leo variant was deployed in the course of the March fighting in Tetovo, which is in line with the statements of various newspaper articles (the Spiegel article even includes a photo of a Leo 2 A4). However, Zwilling links the aforementioned March battles with the image of a Leopard 2 A4, which, as one can see from its labels, was obviously part of the NATO operation Essential Harvest. This operation was not carried out until August 22, 2001. This photo is interesting because it proves the deployment of German Leopard 2 A4s in the Essential Harvest operation. At the end of June, it was still utterly open whether the Bundeswehr would participate in this operation at all. According to an article in the Frankfurter Allgemeine Zeitung dated August 28, 2001, the Bundeswehr was preparing at that time to deploy, among other things, eight battle tanks, which were to be transferred from Kosovo to Macedonia.

During Essential Harvest, no combat operations are documented. An interview with Oberst Harder, commander of the Macedonian contingent, on August 29, 2001, clarifies that the Leopard tanks were transferred to Macedonia solely for a show of force or as a quick reaction force, but did not actively participate in the disarmament of the UÇK.

Leopard 2 at the Hindu Kush

Before the deployment of Danish tanks at the Hindu Kush, a research group led by Canada on-site in Afghanistan investigated which modifications were necessary on the Leo 2 to prepare it optimally for this mission. The Danes participated in the investigations and discussed tactical and logistical challenges in this context. The results were incorporated into the upgrades of the Leopard 2 of both nations and their operational doctrine and supply.

The Leopard 2 A6M of the Canadian Army leased by Germany immediately reinforced the Leopard 1 C2s in Afghanistan. A total of 14 Leopard 2 A6M CANs were designated for active service in the Hindu Kush alongside six Leopard 1 C2s. Six more Leopard 2s were held back as a reserve. The crews of the first two Leo 2 rotations had been trained since May 2007 in Munster by the German tank force as well as in the Netherlands.

The first Leo 2 arrived at Kandahar Airfield in August 2007 and was not yet fitted with slat armor, desert camouflage paint job, and the barracuda thermal mat system – the air conditioning was also retrofitted on-site later. However, sources contradict each other on this very upgrade. Alternatively, the crews continued to wear cooling vests as in the Leo 1, which were cooled down by a cryogenic plant. C Squadron of The Lord Strathcona's Horse (Royal Canadians) provided the first rotation personnel. In September 2007, all 20 Leo 2s were in Afghanistan. The transfer of Canadian tanks from Germany to the Hindu Kush is symbolic of modern military operations' international character: A Ukrainian Antonov An-124 heavy-duty aircraft transported the panzers to Kandahar Airfield where they were loaded onto trucks rented from the Netherlands for further overland transport.

After checking all arms in a practice shooting, the Canadian Leos regularly took part in patrols in armored and partially armored columns. They were also deployed in emplacements to guards the camp, the Forward Operating Base Ma'Sum Ghar in Panjwai. At times, the Canadians used both Leopard models at the same time, as the Leo 2 could not initially be equipped with dozer blades and other tools. The tanks also served as a quick reaction force.

Since September 2007, the Canadian Leopards have participated in all primary operations of the Kandahar Task Force (a U.S.-Canadian formation responsible for the province of Kandahar and was under the authority of Regional Command South). In addition to armor-piercing ammunition and multi-purpose rounds, the Canadians used canister rounds with some success, especially against groups of insurgents and enemies entrenched behind clay walls. With one round, 1,100 small balls are fired at the target.

The Danish Armed Forces were expanding their involvement in ISAF suggestively. On 1 June 2007, due to the difficult security situation and the extension of ISAF's responsibilities, Copenhagen decided to increase the Danish engagement in the south of Afghanistan. The Danish contingent called DANCON ISAF Stage 3 was to grow to a battle group under the command of the Helmand Task Force in Helmand Province (an international formation led by the United Kingdom, which exercised the ISAF mandate in Helmand Province under the command of Regional Command Southwest). Denmark expected that this step would lead to more enemy contacts. Interestingly, the sources do not mention any societal debate about the deployment of Danish battle tanks whatsoever, as had been observed for Canada in the deployment of Leopard 1s to Afghanistan. What the sources do mention is a debate within the Danish military. Concerns were expressed that the deployment of tanks in the Hindu Kush could make the Taliban and other insurgents appear even more aggressive.

In September 2007, one tank Deling with 15 soldiers, equipped with three Leopard 2 A5 DK main battle tanks plus one reserve panzer (only Schulze (2011) speaks of two reserve panzers) plus one M113 armored personnel carrier plus one Cougar 6x6 plus one recovery tank were prepared in Denmark for deployment in Helmand. The Deling was designated Kampvognsdetachement, short TANKDET. From time to time, the personnel and material composition of the TANKDET changed slightly, and later a mobile electronic warfare team was added, among others; however, it always consisted of three Leopard 2s plus reserve. All Leopards were equipped with the modifications described in the chapter "Users" for deployment abroad except for the mine protection package, which was later retrofitted in response to an IED attack. The slat armor was mounted around summer 2008, according to the photographs in Thomas Antonsen's book. The M113 carried a British radio operator who ensured contact between the British leadership and the Danes and a jammer to suppress mobile radio frequencies.

Danish parliament approved the transfer of the tanks on October 23, 2007. The decision to send Leopards to Afghanistan was driven by Oberstøjtnant Jan Grünberger, commander of DANCON 3 (the number stands for the rotation, so this is the third one; Danish rotations always served for six months in the Hindu Kush: February to August and August to February), and his successor, Oberst Kim Kristensen, who both understood the need for MBTs in Afghanistan.

The Leopards were transported by plane (Antonov An-124-100) to Kandahar, from where the tanks moved to FOB Sandford in Helmand Province. The first Leo arrived in Kandahar shortly after October 25. In November 2007, the TANKDET reported combat readiness. The FOB Sandford served as its base; the reserve vehicle was located in Camp Bastion. The TANKDET operated in Afghanistan as an autonomous unit, reporting directly to the battle group commander. The personnel of the 1st rotation was provided mainly by the Jydske Dragonregiment. Kaptajn Bjarne appeared as the commander of the Eskadron. Premierløjtnant Ulrik commanded the troop. (For the Danish involvement in the Hindu Kush, for most soldiers, only rank and first name are given in the source material.)

At the same time, the Danish Armed Forces took over their own area of responsibility in the province of Helmand with the Nahr-e Saraj district. A supply element responsible for all logistical tasks for the Danish ISAF contingent was stationed in Camp Bastion. Two mechanics from the Danish Armored Forces were located in Sandford, so numerous maintenance and repair jobs were carried out there. Once a month, the Leos redeployed to Bastion for more thorough maintenance. Krauss-Maffei Wegmann's customer service mechanics were there to help out with repairs.

The Danish tankers regularly took part in camp guarding duties to be informed immediately from which direction and in which strength the enemy was engaged in case of an attack on the FOB.

In addition to making up the quick reaction force, the Danish Leos' range of tasks included escorting convoys, surveillance assignments, securing temporary checkpoints and operations that were meant to foster ISAF's influence in the region. As a result, the Danish tanks were involved in the majority of the battle group's operations. Furthermore, they operated in the Southwest in more extensive operations of the Helmand Task Force and Regional Command. The Danish Leos' combat loads included HEAT rounds, sabot rounds (anti-tank), and canister rounds, and PELE ammunition (for penetrating concrete walls, for example).

In the first few months, the deployment of the Leopard 2 A6M for a Canadian tank crew already proved to be life-saving when, on November 2, 2007, their panzer was struck by an IED hidden at the roadside 10 kilometers north of the Arghandāb. The driver suffered from a broken hip, but he was alive, and the rest of the crew remained unharmed. In a letter of thanks to the German Federal Ministry of Defense, the tank's commander stated that his crew in any other vehicle would probably not have survived. Although the IED had temporarily incapacitated the Leo 2 A6M, it was already back in action following repairs on-site.

On November 10, the Danish Leos took part in Operation Green Fleet, which involved a convoy of almost 100 vehicles under British command moving from Kandahar to Camp Bastion. The convoy stretched over four kilometers and had to cover a distance of about 140 kilometers, which took almost 24 hours. The only incident worth mentioning occurred in downtown Kandahar when reports came in that the Taliban could launch an attack under cover of the crowds in the city center. In fact, the Danish tankers leading the convoy spotted a truck ahead, which stopped in front of them before two men left it and ran away abruptly. Sergent Bjarke, commander of this same tank with the call sign 2, instructed his driver to push the truck off the road. No sooner said than done; no attack happened. The rest of the motor march went without any incidents; the tankers slept in their vehicles in turn.

On November 17, 2007, the three active tanks of the TANKDET traveled on to Camp Sandford.

On November 24, 2007, the first shot in anger was fired by a Danish Leopard during a patrol conducted by the TANKDET together with infantrymen from the mechanized Den Kongelige Livgarde Regiment north of the FOB Sandford. The patrol's objective was to provoke some Taliban response. In the vicinity of two buildings, the infantrymen spotted three Taliban fighters hiding in a row of trees. The Danish infantrymen attacked them and killed one of the insurgents. The other two fled in the direction of the buildings. Sergent Bjarke's tank fired at them at a distance of a little more than 1,000 meters with its coaxial machine gun. After about 50 shots without hits, Bjarke ordered to switch to the main armament. The gunner then fired a HEAT round, into whose explosion the two Taliban disappeared. The buildings, only 15 to 20 meters from the impact, remained completely undamaged, and there were no wounded among the Danish infantrymen who had sought cover in one of those buildings. After the incident, the Danes withdrew to FOB Sandford under cover fire from their mortars.

After that, the TANKDET participated as a fire support element in numerous operations in the Helmand River area, which is known as the Green Zone; for example, in December 2007, during the dismantling of FOB Arnhem on the east bank, where the Danish Leos stayed on site for a total of three weeks to guard the process. During this time, the insurgents fired a missile at the FOB. Otherwise, there was no enemy contact. The tanks often took up positions in elevated areas to provide immediate fire support for troops operating in the Green Zone.

In the desert outside the Green Zone, the Danish Leos initially enjoyed a freedom of movement that was not granted to later rotations anymore. The insurgents were soon to understand to secure areas with mines and IEDs against Leopard operations.

In November, Sergent Bjarke's tank was hit by a mine or an IED without seriously wounding the crew members.

On 5 January 2008, a significant skirmish between Taliban fighters and the Danish TANKDET took place in the Green Zone. The latter initially took up elevated positions to monitor Danish (west bank) and British (east bank) soldiers operating in the Green Zone on both river banks. The infantrymen advanced north to drive the Taliban further away from the more populated areas between FOB Sandford and the town of Girishk. Around 11:00 hrs, the British came under fire from the Taliban entrenched on the east bank. Shortly afterward, insurgents opened fire on the Danish infantry from the west bank. In addition, several rockets were fired at the Leopards. Sergent Bjarke identified an insurgent with a recoilless B-10 gun in a building. He ordered to fire a HEAT round at him. But even after that, the Leos were still under fire from several positions with rocket launchers and similar weapons. The other tanks opened up on the enemy too and shot at identified enemy positions and Taliban fighters who ventured out of cover. In the end, the Leopards had fired 25 rounds of their main armaments. The battle ended after two hours of fierce fighting. ISAF air support bombed two buildings, in which several Taliban fighters hid. The insurgents withdrew, and the area remained free of the enemy for several weeks. The Danish tanker Jacob (rank unclear), loader of the tank with call sign 3, was wounded in this battle; he suffered frostbite of the second degree on his buttocks. How could this happen? An unfortunate chain of events led to this very special wound, which earned him the nickname "Jacob Frozen Ass": After the second shot was fired, the cartridge case fell so unluckily onto the first case, which was already in the collection container that a spark arose, which triggered the fire extinguishing system. It pumped Jacob a shot of ice-cold halon directly against his butt.

Ulrik, who is quoted in Thomas Antonsen's book, assesses the Taliban's behavior in this battle as professional, coordinated, and geared to taking out a Leopard 2.

Also, in January 2008, Danish Leopards provided fire support for another encounter between British troops and Taliban fighters.

After the rotation change to DANCON 5, the Leo with call sign 3 hit a Soviet tank mine on February 22, 2008. The track was thrown in the explosion, and two road wheels were blown off. The other Leopard tanks immediately formed a ring around the immobilized vehicle, while the Taliban debated on an attack on the tanks by radio but did not carry it out. The crew of the struck tank remained unharmed and quickly pulled the track back on. Despite the missing road wheels, the Leopard was able to drive the approximately 80 kilometers to Camp Bastion under its own power, where it was repaired. A total of ten times during Dancon 5, a Leo hit a mine or was struck by an IED.

Frankfurter Allgemeine reported a similar incident that is said to have happened on February 26, 2008, which reads almost the same as the incident on February 22, 2008, so I suspect it is the same one; either the Frankfurter Allgemeine or Antonsen got the date wrong.

In early March, the TANKDET moved to Forward Operating Base Armadillo, four kilometers north of FOB Sandford. Armadillo's infrastructure was downright feudal, which is why the tankers spent a lot of time and energy to develop it.

On March 31, 2008, the Danish Leopards participated in Operation Tufaan Dervish II, aiming to reconnoiter and attack insurgents north of FOB Sandford and push the enemy further back. Previously, Danish infantry units had already been under enemy fire several times from there. With Tufaan Dervish II, the Danes deployed strong forces of their battle group to drive back the enemy and hold the won terrain. The TANKDET was divided into two groups for this purpose: the first group, led by the commander of the Deling, Colonel Løjtnant Martin (Leopard with the call sign 3), consisted of the M113, which transported British pioneers, in addition to Leopard tanks. The second group consisted of the Leopard with call sign 2, the recovery tank, Danish pioneers, and an infantry platoon. The insurgents had already understood at that time that the Danish tanks could only be met with booby traps and mines. Gone were the days of absolute freedom of movement. Now the pioneers had to search every square meter with mine detectors before the Leopards could drive through. It was a dangerous task for the dismounted pioneers and also slowed down all tank operations. The two groups were deployed directly in the Green Zone, where they were to clear safe access lanes at a distance of 1,500 to 2,000 meters from each other.

Operation Tufaan Dervish II began at 05:00 hrs on that March 31, 2008, and only a short time later, the pioneers searching the ground in front of the tanks encountered the first IED when RPGs were fired at them from a building some 700 meters away, only just missing them by an inch. Martin reacted quickly and commanded both his tank and call sign 3 to batter said building with HEAT rounds. After the enemy fire had subsided, the pioneers resumed their work. In this way, the NATO soldiers slowly worked their way forward. After gaining a few hundred meters of terrain, insurgents from the same building opened fire again with RPGs. This time they apparently aimed directly at the Leopards. Six more multi-purpose rounds were fired at the building before the TANKDET's forward air controller called for an airstrike. Simultaneously, the other group came under fire, resulting in fighting two Taliban in close combat (less than 300 meters) with canister rounds.

Afterward, the Danish infantry advanced at a speed at which the tanks could no longer follow because the searching pioneers still slowed them down. Martin decided to let the pioneers stop their mine detection work to catch up with the infantry. Without incident, his group reached a vantage point from where he could monitor the infantry's progress. He watched the population flee the area – usually a sure sign of an imminent insurgent attack. Then an IED blew up in front of the infantry, killing one soldier and seriously wounding two. Martin spotted Taliban fighters in

81

the forefield and opened fire on them. A radio message came in that the IED triggerman was trying to leave the battlefield on a motorcycle. The Leo with call sign 3 spotted the fugitive and shot him with a HEAT round. The infantrymen were still in enemy contact in the forefield of the tanks. The dense vegetation made the situation unclear, so they could not evacuate the wounded. They marked an identified enemy position with yellow smoke, and Martin's group broke any enemy resistance with another HEAT round. The Danes were then able to bring out their wounded. The TANKDET used a total of 21 multi-purpose rounds, 2 canister rounds, and about 500 machine gun bullets in this battle.

Besides, during their mission in the Hindu Kush, the Danish tankers set up several firing positions, including alternate positions in elevated areas from where they could overlook the Green Zone along the Helmand. The insurgents quickly began to mine these positions and the access routes. Thomas Antonsen quotes TANKDET Commander Martin as saying that deploying Leopard 2s in Helmand Province often prevented the insurgents from going into battle, as they were not able to do much against tanks, but in return had to expect to be fired on at long distances, even if visibility conditions were poor.

In April 2008, the Canadian Leopards 2 in Afghanistan were retrofitted with Barracuda thermal mats, which reduced the heat signature and reduced the heat problem in the tanks' fighting compartment. The Danes also had gathered good experience with this system.

In the summer of 2008, Canadians and insurgents fought bitterly for Strongpoint Mushan, located in the remote Panjwai district on the peninsula between Arghandāb and Dori. They were only established that year, some 20 kilometers from the city of Mushan. The Canadian Armed Forces were on site with the Operational Mentor and Liaison Team (OMLT) 71A from 3rd Battalion, Princess Patricia's Canadian Light Infantry. The team consisted of four soldiers, accompanying 1st Company of 1st Kandak of 1st Brigade of 205th Corps of the ANA, commanded by Colonel Anwar. At that time, B Squadron of Strathcona's under Major Chris Adams served with the Canadian Leopard 2 tanks in Afghanistan.

Insurgents dominated the northern riverbank of Arghandāb. In June 2008, the situation at Strongpoint Mushan came to a head. Every patrol that left the base came under fire. Enemy mortar troops battered the strongpoint's vicinity, with impacts reaching up to 100 meters from the outer walls. The Canadians then launched Operation Room Service to reinforce Strongpoint Mushan with an additional instructor for the Afghan forces and five ANA soldiers. These were to be brought in via an armored column consisting of Canadian Leopard 2s, among others.

In the subsequent Operation Nolai on June 14, 2008, Strongpoint Mushan forces deployed a platoon of soldiers and two instructors to cross the river and distract the Taliban entrenched on the other side, who were then to be attacked by mechanized Canadian and Afghan forces. The plan failed because of the Taliban's heavy defensive fire. The Mushan forces withdrew again, and the base was then fired on with mortars. In the course of that bombardment, an Afghan officer and a Canadian instructor were wounded. The mechanized column of Operation Room Service left Strongpoint Mushan shortly afterward.

The fighting for the base intensified in the following days. When Canadian and/or ANA troops left the base, they immediately came under fire, at the latest by the riverbed. The strongpoint was fired upon with RPGs, a recoilless 82-millimeter gun, small arms, and mortars. The Canadians responded with airstrikes, mortars, and shots from their Carl Gustav, while the ANA soldiers attacked with Ford Ranger cars with mounted 12.7-millimeter MGs. The Mushan forces soon ran out of ammunition. On July 4, the strongpoint again came under heavy barrage fire, wounding five Afghan soldiers and taking out the Canadians' mortar. One Afghan died from his wounds, while the Mushan base ran out of medical supplies.

On July 5, 2008, B Squadron once again deployed their Leopards in a mechanized column to carry out Operation Room Service 2. Strongpoint Mushan had to be resupplied, and the Canadians and Afghans stationed there were to be replaced. Part of the column were Ford

Rangers of the ANA. Even the access route, which was only a little more than 20 kilometers long, turned into running the gauntlet. Several times along the banks of the Arghandāb River, there were contacts with insurgents. The column was finally welcomed outside the base's walls by OMLT 71A and the Afghan 1st Company. For them, 71B and 2nd Company of the Kandak took over. On the way back, the column again came under heavy fire. The Leopard 2 A6Ms responded with their 120-millimeter cannons, while Captain Matt Aggus of 71A, under tank fire cover, led an Afghan dismounted raiding party that took up the fight. The attackers fled.

Only 600 meters further on, the column was fired upon again. On both sides of the river, small arms barked, and RPGs hissed. ANA and ISAF troops returned fire. It became frantic when a Taliban fighter, armed with an RPG, ran head-on at two Leopards. The commanders briefly coordinated their actions, and then each fired a multi-purpose round at the attacker, literally tearing him to shreds.

At the end of July 2008, Operation Room Service 3 was carried out, and once again, the Leopards of B Squadron accompanied the column. 71B and the Afghan 2nd Company returned to Strongpoint Mushan. The Leopards stayed there for at least two nights. On the first night, the insurgents tried to hit the tanks with a total of 7 mortar rounds. Also, on the second night, the Leopards were shelled by high-angle fire. Thereupon two U.S. F-18s bombed the suspected mortar position. Insurgents hanging about outside the strongpoint were greeted by the Leopards with 120-millimeter rounds and then fled. A total of five insurgents were killed that night. Shortly after, the Leopards returned to Ma'Sum Ghar.

For the tank soldiers of DANCON 5, the death of one of their comrades became a defining event during their six months in Afghanistan: on July 25, 2008, the driver of the Leopard with call sign 2, Jesper Gilbert Pedersen, were killed on patrol on the west side of the Helmand River. On that day, the TANKDET supported an operation by the ANA and their British mentors against the Taliban about 4 kilometers north of FOB Armadillo. After the ANA had simulated an IED attack with a controlled explosion to draw out the Taliban, a spotter of the enemy appeared quite conspicuously, coordinating mortar fire against the Danish tanks. A few salvos from the Leopards' coaxial machine gun made him flee, after which the high-angle fire died down. Thereupon the TANKDET changed position over an alley cleared by the pioneers beforehand. At one point in this alley, the tanks had to make a sharp 90-degree turn. When the Leo with call sign 2 (Commander: Mikkel – rank unclear) performed the maneuver, an IED struck. For a few moments, the intercom failed; after that, Mikkel could call his crew members. Dramatic seconds followed: loader and gunner reported ready for action, but driver Pedersen remained silent. Since the turret was turned to the side, the other crew members could not reach him.

To make matters worse, the engine was still running; the tank continued to roll and moved towards a 10 to 15 meters steep downslope. Mikkel ordered his crew to dismount. All three jumped from the moving tank and suffered impact injuries. The Leopard rolled towards the downslope but got stuck just before it and stopped.

The wounded were immediately evacuated and flown to Camp Bastion. The tank was recovered and taken to an ANA base nearby, where Pedersen's death was ascertained. It turned out that the IED had blown up directly under the driver's emergency exit hatch, and he had had no chance of survival in the resulting blast.

The Danish Army Combat Centre took the incident as an opportunity to retrofit its Leos 2s deployed in Afghanistan with the mine protection package from the M upgrade.

In August 2008, the rotation change (DANCON 6) took place, 2nd Eskadron of 1st Panserbataljons of the Jydske Dragonregiment provided the TANKDET personnel. With the change of the rotation, the tankers' mission was also extended: The protection of the town of Girishk from Taliban attacks and securing its reconstruction were added. Girishk is a town some 110 kilometers northeast of Kandahar on the banks of the Helmand River. On the many rides through Girishk during the years of their ISAF mission, the Danish tanks were occasionally pelted with stones or vegetables. The call signs were also altered with the ration change: the TANKDET was now called Alpha Troop, led by Premierløjtnant Jens.

In September 2008, Canadian and Afghan forces were withdrawn from Strongpoint Mushan, while Canadian sappers went to work on site. The supply of the base was moved into the air. Although not explicitly documented, it is likely, Canadian Leopards were also used to extract the Mushan forces in September 2008 and to transport the pioneers safely.

A Danish Leopard 2A5 is passing through Main Operation Base (MOB) Price in October 2008. Shortly before, the Danish Leopard 2s were equipped with slat armor elements to protect the vehicles from RPG rounds. During DANCON 6 (August 2008 – February 2009), the Leopard 2s were operated by crews from 2nd Tank Squadron of 1st Armored Battalion of the Jutland Dragoons Regiment, as can be seen from the unit pennant on the turret antenna (Copyright Danish Defence Command)

On November 14, 2008, the Danish TANKDET returned from a patrol to FOB Armadillo. As soon as the tankers had left their vehicles, the camp was hit by an 82-millimeter projectile of a B-10 recoilless rifle. The round hit a storehouse just a few meters from Jens and one of his tank commanders, and the blast wave swept them off their feet. They remained uninjured. The following day, the B-10 recoilless rifle was identified in a cave entrance. After an airstrike failed, Alpha Troop moved out and destroyed the gun with a multi-purpose round.

On 16 and 17 November 2008, the Danish TANKDET supported a British operation with two Leopard tanks (Premierløjtnant Jens and Sergent Chris, call sign 2) south of Camp Bastion. The aim was to establish contact with the enemy to ascertain his location and strength. Around noon, the two Leopard tanks left camp together with other troops to unite with British recce forces (British Brigade Reconnaissance Force). Together they then moved south, the Leopards forming the closing element of the column. At 17:00 hrs, the column reached the agreed meeting point with British Special Forces (Taskforce 444), who had set up a harbor from which they observed the area. After a sitrep and a rest period, the tanks rolled southwards from 02:00 hrs onwards, where they reached the next meeting point at around 04:30 hrs. At 07:00 hrs, the British reconnaissance forces reported enemy contact. Shortly after that, the Special Forces reported the same. The Leopards set off together with a British escort in the direction of Task Force 444. The mounted Special Forces were engaged in a firefight with two insurgents who entrenched themselves in a graveyard. After several changes of position, Chris' tank fired several warning shots with the MG. A third insurgent then appeared, only 800 meters away from Chris. He took cover and fired his Kalashnikov at the Danish tanks. Jens' gunner returned fire first with the coaxial MG, causing the assailant to flee behind the protection of a wall, from where he started firing again. A HEAT round tore the wall to pieces and finally killed the attacker.

The Leopards then moved in the direction of the British recce forces. Along the way, they came under small-caliber and RPG fire, but could not identify the attackers' positions, so they broke through to the British, who were also under fire without being able to spot the enemy. The British and Danes then withdrew.

In early December, Sergent Chris' tank was struck by an IED on the way back from Armadillo to Camp Bastion. The blast shredded the track and some road wheels and tore off part of the slat armor. Commander and gunner looked out of the hatch at this time; the torn off armor elements flew just above their heads. Immediately the pioneers searched the area. The damage could not be repaired on-site, so Premierløjtnant Jens' tank towed the damaged Leo back to Armadillo. There it was repaired in a makeshift way to make the way to Bastion by its own power. When the tank arrived at the camp, it was discovered that the hull was so warped by the explosion that the tank had to be decommissioned.

With the switch to DANCON 7 in February 2009, Premierløjtnant Dennis took over command of the TANKDET. From April to mid-July 2009, the Helmand Task Force carried out a series of operations under the name Panther's Claw. The aim was to conquer and hold the village of Spin Masjed, which connected the two important cities of Girishk and Lashkar Gah. The background was the elections scheduled for August 20. The TANKDET was regularly used to provide fire support and monitor the actions of the troops carrying out Operation Panther's Claw.

In April 2009, the Danish tanks moved their base from Armadillo to the Main Operating Base Price west of Girishk. (The FOBs Sandford and Armadillo were located east of and far from the city).

A Danish Leopard 2 A5 somewhere in the Afghan desert during DANCON 8 (August 2009 to February 2010). The vehicles were equipped with Barracuda thermal mats from the Swedish company SAAB (Copyright Danish Defence Command, Anders Fridberg)

On June 20, the Danish tanks once again took up their elevated positions to monitor the Green Zone. Suddenly the crew of the Leo with call sign 2 reported explosions directly in front of their vehicle. From his position, the commander of the M113 could see a group of Taliban firing RPGs into the air below the tank positions to hit the Leos. An airstrike was called in via the Forward

Air Controller. Thus an F-15 Strike Eagle shot at the Taliban with its 20-millimeter Gatling. The insurgents then fled. The Strike Eagle rounds hit so close to the tank with call sign 2 that its gunner described the moments of the impacts as dramatic.

Also, in June, a significant operation of the Danes took place. One early morning, several Danish units encircled a group of Taliban north of FOB Armadillo in a horseshoe shape formation. The aim was to drive the insurgents towards the Leopard tanks, which blocked the "horseshoe" opening. After some time, an armed man approached the tanks up to 200 meters; he was obviously in a firefight with Danish infantry driving him. The Leo with call sign 2 killed him with machine gunfire. 10 to 15 minutes later, a second insurgent, armed with a machine gun, appeared. Call sign 2 fired at him with a multi-purpose round. Shortly after that, two men approached armed with an RPG-7. One Leo shot at them with a multi-purpose round at a distance of 1,600 meters. It hit a tree, tore it to shreds, and killed the two insurgents in the process. Further attackers were subsequently engaged before two men were spotted in a wadi to the left of the Leopard with call sign 2. Since the tank was still fighting other targets, the gunner attacked the two men from his hatch with his carbine M/96 (Colt Canada C8 Carbine). He pinned them down, firing a total of more than five magazines before the gunner was able to turn the turret and engaged with two canister rounds, killing the insurgents.

End of June, the TANKDET was reinforced by a Wisent recovery tank converted to a mine-clearing tank, which meant that pioneers no longer had to dismount to search for mines and IEDs. Demining routes were now 15 to 20 times faster.

On July 2, 2009, a task force consisting of British, Afghan and Danish troops, including their Leos, advanced through the Nahr-E-Bughra Channel as part of Operation Panther's Claw. The tanks secured the other forces while crossing the channel. This operation was the first time that the Wisent mentioned above was used, which shortly afterward hit an IED and was incapacitated for the time being.

On July 8, the task force again operated at the Nahr-E-Bughra Channel. The TANKDET was divided into two groups for this operation. Two tanks were positioned on the west bank of the channel as fire support for a British operation. The Leopard with call sign 3 crossed the channel and guarded Danish infantry east of the crossing as they proceeded. Around 08:00 hrs, call sign 3 broke through a hedge, but then the crew realized that the infantry did not follow. The driver backed the tank. In the process, a tree trunk got wedged so severely in the running gear that the Leo threw its track and got stuck. The rest of the TANKDET rushed to the rescue but could not recover the tank because of the soft ground. In Camp Price, there was still a Leopard 1-based recovery tank (Bergepanzer 2), which had been temporarily shut down. In a hurry, a crew was gathered to get the ARV ready for action and immediately set off for the position of the TANKDET. The tank was finally recovered from the Green Zone and towed by two Leos to MOB Price.

With the change of rotation in August 2009, Premierløjtnant Erik took command of the TANKDET. The tankers of DANCON 9 were initially mainly engaged in maintenance and repair works, as the activities during Operation Panther's Claw had left their mark.

Meanwhile, the Taliban threatened to interfere with the August 20 elections, so DANCON stationed a part of its TANKDET at Artillery Hill, an ANA artillery barracks on the eastern bank Helmand River, within reach of a vital bridge over the same water and within sight of Girishk. When the polling booths opened, insurgents fired a mortar, which was observed by the Danish Leo crew with call sign 2 as well as by Danish snipers. An artillery strike did not succeed, so the Leo finally received fire clearance after the attackers had fired a second shot. They were able to put the attackers to rout with two multi-purpose rounds at a distance of 3,800 meters.

In Thomas Antonsen's book, Erik reports about another enemy contact. It remains unclear when exactly it happened: At least one Leopard was monitoring the actions of a reconnaissance unit through a cornfield in Pasab. The goal was to reach a channel where enemy contact had already been made earlier. No sooner had the recce troops reached that channel than they came under heavy defensive fire. The Leopard or Leopards first entered the firefight with their machine guns, and then they fought identified targets with their main cannon. At the same time, another Leo 2 entered the battlefield and also opened fire. Later, an RPG projectile detonated near the TANKDET's M113. Finally, the Taliban's main emplacement was reconnoitered and eliminated with an airstrike.

In September 2009, the TANKDET was assigned for five days to secure another crossing over the Helmand.

The first week of December 2009 was dedicated to Operation Cobra's Anger. The U.S. Marines Corps was in charge of this operation and explicitly requested battle tanks, as they had no own MBTs in Afghanistan at their disposal. The goal was to liberate Now Zad, about 80 kilometers north of Girishk, and to eliminate all IED threats there. Now Zad had been under Taliban control for two years. Under greatest secrecy, a British logistics unit transported the parachute-covered Leopard tanks to the deployment area in a one-and-a-half-day motor march. On the way, one of the heavy transporters was incapacitated by an IED attack. Since the Danish tank drivers accompanied the column (the rest of the crews was transported to the deployment area by helicopter), the Leo was able to travel the rest of the route under its own steam.

The Marines and Danes found Now Zad deserted. Soon, however, the Marines became involved in smaller skirmishes with Taliban fighters. Furthermore, the city center turned out to be contaminated with IEDs. The Marines saw no other option but to blow up whole parts of the city in a controlled manner. Shortly before Christmas, the Danes arrived back at MOB Price.

On December 29 to 31, 2009, Canadian Leopard 2s (B Squadron) took part in Operation Toffan. Together with other Kandahar Task Force troops, they fought to keep the Isa Dora-Lalique Corridor in southwestern Kandahar free of insurgents.

On December 30, 2009, an ISAF column clashed with insurgents in the context of Operation Toffan. The Leopard 2 A6M CANs of the QRF opened fire on the enemy from an armored column with their main armaments. Besides, Canadian Leos with pre-stressed mine rollers paved the way through mine-, UXO- and IED-infested terrain during the operation. The value of the mine rollers was proven when a Leopard 2 triggered an IED with them. Neither the vehicle nor the rollers were damaged during the detonation.

For a major operation in 2010, the Danish TANKDET and a platoon of a Danish reconnaissance battalion were combined to form Task Force Beast, commanded by Premierløjtnant Erik. TF Beast was given the task of conducting a diversionary maneuver. To this end, it was to patrol the area east of the Helmand River between FOB Khar Nikah and Highway 611 in order to distract from operations west of the river. For six days, TF Beast set up temporary checkpoints along the highway, conducted reconnaissance work, and secured river crossings. One assignment even involved medical care for a village in the area of operations. The mission was a success, with the primary operations west of the river being carried out in part without the Taliban noticing.

In February 2010, the Danish contingent rotated to DANCON 9, and cooperation with the Afghan security authorities intensified at this time, with the Danish battle group showing a high level of activity overall. The command of the TANKDET was taken over by Premierløjtnant Martin (not the same person as Premierløjtnant Martin from DANCON 5).

With the British Operation Moshtarak under British command, the Danish Leos of DANCON 5 had their first principal combat mission. The aim was to liberate Marjah, located southwest of Lashkar Gah, from the Taliban and drug traffickers. Simultaneously, several observation posts had to be set up along the highway that runs parallel to Helmand River. For the three-week operation, the TANKDET, including the Wisent and two supply trucks, was placed under British recce troops' command. The Danes and British set up a temporary base at an Afghan National Police checkpoint near Helmand's Bolan Bridge as a starting point for all operations. On the way to the area of deployment, the Danish tankers struggled with various technical defects, which meant that one of the Leos was only partially operational. No radio contact could be established with the British via the radio equipment of the M113. As a result, Sergent Heine, commander of the partially defective tank, was put at the British's disposal as a liaison man. Interesting in this context is the verdict of Premierløjtnant Martin, which is printed in Thomas Antonsen's book: With only one supply trip and the one-time flying in of a team of mechanics, the Leopards were able to operate utterly autonomous over the entire span of three weeks despite the technical problems.

On the morning of February 13, 2010, Heine participated in a British patrol on foot at the Bolan Bridge to provoke a Taliban reaction; the Danish Leopards initially oversaw the course of action.

After some time, Heine reported enemy contact to TANKDET commander Martin. The British patrol was pinned down and already had a wounded man, but the tanks could not intervene due to the confusing terrain. Only the firing of a Hellfire missile by an Apache made the insurgents' fire die away.

Martin's statement on Operation Moshtarak in Antonsen's book suggests that further enemy contacts were made during the operation. The enemy often retreated as soon as the Danish Leos entered the battlefield.

In the afternoon of May 4, 2010, the Taliban launched a concentrated attack on the Danish-held Patrol Base Bridzar on the edge of those heights from which the Green Zone could be monitored well. By the evening, the Danes had already 11 wounded (out of a total of around 20 soldiers) who could not be flown out due to a sandstorm. A Danish-British task force was therefore gathered, including the TANKDET. Premierløjtnant Martin assumed the overall command. The motor march from MOB Price to Patrol Base Clifton, one kilometer north of Bridzar, covered a distance of 15 kilometers, but the raging sandstorm limited the view to a few meters. The march lasted three hours. Two British vehicles and a Danish one malfunctioned and had to be escorted back to Price by Danish military police or pioneers, which reduced the strength of the task force by more than half. Martin made the decision to march from Clifton to Bridzar on foot, fearing that more vehicles would be incapacitated due to the sandstorm. The soldiers in Brizdar were finally reinforced, and the wounded could be removed without resorting to the Leopard tanks.

With the next rotation change in August 2010, being part of the quick reaction force defined the Danish tankers' everyday life for three months. They also once again provided fire support for numerous operations in the Green Zone. The last three months were focused on operations on the Helmand River's east bank along Highway 611. The Leopards also escorted numerous columns in the area of responsibility, mainly between the various FOBs, MOBs, and camps. Premierløjtnant Troels was in command of the TANKDET. During the period of DANCON 10, expansion works of this highway were given high priority due to its importance as a connecting road. The Taliban killed more than 20 men of a private security company at the construction site in several attacks. Hence, ISAF assigned a security force consisting of British, US-Americans, and Danes, including their Leos, for the further construction work. It was enough to stop all significant Taliban attacks. Major-General Richard Mills of the U.S. Marines Corps assessed the Danish battle tanks' appearance as decisive for the Taliban to refrain from further action.

Nevertheless, the TANKDET was repeatedly involved in smaller skirmishes along with the construction site, for example, on November 5, 2010. In the afternoon of that day, the Danish tankers with their panzers had established a harbor within sight of the construction work when a single attacker opened fire with a Russian PKM machine gun whose salvos hit the tanks. Sergeant Jesper, commander of the tank with call sign 2, successfully engaged the attacker with a HEAT round at a distance of 1,680 meters.

In early November 2010, British troops cleared an IED factory in a building east of Girishk. In an attempt to disable the factory, a British pioneer was killed in an IED explosion, so it was decided to use the Danish Leopards' firepower. On the evening of November 9, the battle tanks moved into position within firing range of the IED factory and shot a total of 76 multi-purpose rounds at it over the next half hour, blowing up all IEDs.

The first Canadian Leopard 2 A4 CANs were airlifted to Kandahar in December 2010. By the end of January, five tanks of this variant were in the country, led by the Strathcona's C Squadron soldiers. Already on January 17, 2011, one of these tanks was struck by an IED. The vehicle was damaged, the crew members got away with minor injuries.

For the Danish TANKDET, January 2011 was dominated by British troops' four-day operation in the Green Zone, whose actions were guarded by the tanks. In this context, too, a British officer involved, Captain James Nightingale, emphasized the Leos' deterrent effect on the insurgents. There was no contact with the enemy during this operation.

For DANCON 11 (February 2011 to August 2011), the Jydske Dragonregiment provided the crews of the TANKDET, led by Premierløjtnant Christian. The main focus was on Girishk and a line of patrol bases east of it. First, the Danish tanks assisted in February 2010 in dismantling FOB Armadillo, which was subsequently handed over to the ANA. During the last stay in the base, the Leopards were observed by suspected Taliban fighters, but no attack took place.

Leopard 2 A4M CANs operated with pre-stressed mine rollers in the Arghandāb valley in March 2011. They participated in similar demining and security operations again and again during the Canadian ISAF mission.

At the end of May, British troops in the FOB Rahim (formerly Sandford) requested tank support from the Danes to ward off repeated attacks on the base. Even after the arrival of the Leos, the attacks continued. On the third day of the Danes' presence, the base came under fire again. British wheeled vehicles, and two of the Danish Leos swarmed out. While the British entered the Green Zone, the first tank (Oversergent Mads) took up an elevated position from where the Green Zone could be overseen. In order to show the insurgents' position in a building, the British marked it with two bursts of fire. Mads fired a shot at the building, then the second Leo reached the elevated position and entered the firefight. After they had fired five multi-purpose rounds, Premierløjtnant Christian in his tank reached the scene of the action. Shortly afterward, the cease-fire order was received. Several insurgents were killed in this incident.

On April 2, 2011, Oversergent Mads' tank was hit by an IED on the Helmand River's eastern bank in the Zumbelay region when the TANKDET assisted British units in the construction of a new Patrol Base south of FOB Keenan. The Danes marched into the target area along a route never before used by ISAF forces to minimize the likelihood of an attack. Nevertheless, at about 14:00 hrs, an explosive device detonated next to Mads' tank with a strength equivalent of 20 to 22.5 kilograms of TNT. The commander briefly lost his memory, and the intercom in his tank helmet suffered a defect. Also, the explosion shredded the track and several road wheels. However, the engine was still running, and the electronics had also remained intact. All crew members were in good health. Christian's Leo dragged the blasted tank back towards Girishk, with the bridge east of the city proving to be a major obstacle as it could not carry two Leopard tanks at the same time. East of the bridge in the desert, the TANKDET met with the QRF, which had been alarmed in the meantime, and brought the ARV Bergepanzer 2 with it. They reached the bridge at about 22:00 hrs. At first, each bank was secured by one Leo 2. In a time-consuming procedure, the ARV then pulled the damaged Leo 2 over the bridge, taking care that always only one vehicle was directly above a bridge pier at a time. The procedure was repeated at a second bridge within Girishk, which also had to be crossed on the way to MOB Price. The TANKDET reached Price between 02:00 and 03:00 hrs at night. The same day the reserve tank was taken out of Camp Bastion to replace the damaged Leo.

In May 2011, the M113 of the TANKDET was replaced by a U.S. Oshkosh MRAP all-terrain vehicle, which promised better protection against mines and IEDs.

In July, the Danish Leos escorted an ISAF convoy.

Premierløjtnant Christian also estimates the Leopards' effect on the insurgents as a deterrent and assumes that the presence of the tanks has minimized enemy contacts. The text supports this hypothesis by John Rugarber. He proves based on a RAND Corporation study that the use of Leopard 2 tanks regularly ensured that the insurgents refrained from a planned attack.

The Canadian Leopard 2s of both variants remained in Afghanistan until July 2011, when Canada ceased its participation in the ISAF mission. Until then, they repeatedly participated in operations against insurgents. In his publication, Carl Schulze mentions four incidents in Afghanistan involving Canadian Leopards struck by mines or IEDs.

Premierløjtnant Anders took command of the TANKDET during DANCON 12. The call sign was A-Troop during this rotation. In September 2011, enemy contact for the new rotation was made for the first time east of Girishk near the Patrol Base line. In the evening of September 4th, the Danish Leopards first reached PB Clifton at the edge of the elevated positions above the Green Zone. During the night, pioneers cleared an area west of the patrol base so that the tankers could set up a harbor there. On September 5, a Danish infantry unit operating nearby reported enemy contact. Anders then divided his tank unit into two groups: he himself stayed in the area with a demining tank and the Oshkosh MRAP, while the second group, consisting of the two remaining Leopards and the Wisent, moved to the area between the two patrol bases Spondon and Bidzar to support the infantry. Later on the way back, the tank with call sign 3 came under fire from close range. It responded with two canister rounds. The group then moved south along the road that connected the patrol bases (Route Sephton). Again they were fired at. This time the enemy had barricaded himself in a building off the road. The two tanks fended the attackers off with HEAT and PELE rounds. PB Spondon reported at this time that they were also under attack. Call sign 3 then drove back to the patrol base when the Leo came under fire from a building east of the road. The insurgents were so close to the Danish tank that the other Leopard could not engage with a HEAT round but fired a PELE round instead. Mortar fire then battered Patrol Base Bidzar, also fired from a building. The second Leo of the group destroyed the mortar with a multi-purpose round. The TANKDET then gathered in PB Clifton. During this mission, the Danish tanks' coordination was enhanced because they had numbered the buildings along Route Sephton in advance to speed up communication during battle. In the days that followed, several enemy contacts were made along Route Sephton.

The Danish tanks spent October and November 2011 in FOB Ouellette east of the Helmand River down Route 611 in company of British troops before returning to MOB Price at the end of November.

January was marked by the intention to drive the Taliban off Route Sephton. The patrol base line established there proved not to be sufficient enough for this. In a joint British-Danish-Afghan operation, new patrol bases were set up along the elevated positions above the Green Zone and Girishk, with the Danish Leopards guarding these efforts. Each tanker spent 16 hours a day on active duty.

One morning, tank commander Sergeant Jacob observed an insurgent armed with an RPG crawling about 200 meters away. He reported his discovery, after which first the Leo with call sign 2 and shortly afterward Anders' tank approached from the "break room." The RPG shooter crawled to a haystack, where he readied his weapon. Jacob's Leo, as well as the tank with call sign 2, took him out with HEAT rounds before Anders' tank fired another round at a second insurgent just identified. This second insurgent survived and rushed behind the cover of a wall. Jacob fired a PELE round at the wall. The insurgent was never seen again. After the other two tanks had left the area, Jacob identified a third insurgent who crawled to the undamaged RPG weapon. A meter away from it, the man remained motionless and did not move for half an hour. When he finally reached for the RPG and straightened up, Jacobs shot him with a multi-purpose round. A few days after this incident, the TANKDET returned to MOB Price. For the rest of the rotation period, there were further encounters with insurgents.

90

With DANCON 13 (February 2012 to August 2012), significant changes for the Danish ISAF engagement took place. Deploying an autonomous battle group with its own area of responsibility was abandoned, while the focus shifted to the training of Afghan security authorities. As a result, the TANKDET was directly subordinated to the British Taskforce Helmand, responsible for the former Danish AOR. Commander of the Danish tank unit became Premierløjtnant Kim. A Danish liaison tank officer was sent in the British battle group staff, to which the TANKDET was assigned.

On February 28, 2012, the Wisent of the TANKDET was struck by a powerful IED as the Danish tank unit moved in a column off-road across the desert. All crew members were slightly wounded in the attack, and the vehicle was so severely damaged that it had to be sent back to Denmark for a complete overhaul. However, recovery tanks and a Leo 2 together towed the damaged Wisent to the next paved road, where British recovery troops took over further transport to Camp Bastion. The recovery took more than 24 hours and had to be secured all the way around, and as a direct consequence, the TANKDET had to do without its Wisent for two months, which meant that once again dismounted pioneers had to search the routes in advance for mines and booby traps.

In mid-June 2012, Danish tanks moved to FOB Rahim on the west bank of the Helmand River in an elevated position above the Green Zone, where they participated in a major international operation during the last two weeks of June: Afghan troops patrolled the area along the patrol base line to the area south of Rahim, while Danish infantry operated on the other bank of the river. Simultaneously, U.S. troops operated between FOB Rahim and FOB Budwan (formerly Armadillo), thus surrounding the insurgents. A British infantry company started to enter the insurgents' area and spend the night in different buildings to provoke attacks. During the two weeks, the Danish tanks provided fire support for the infantry operating in the area on several occasions, and the Leopard 2 proved its reputation as a precision instrument when the Danes used it to fight insurgents in close proximity to British troops, for example, without harming the allies.

In July, the Danish Leopards took part in a British-American operation in the extreme southeast of Helmand Province. The aim was to arrest some well-known Taliban fighters. The main task of the Danes was to guard their Allies. In fact, during the operation, which lasted about two weeks, the TANKDET often helped to tow British vehicles to nearby Highway 1 (connecting Kandahar City, Panjwai and Zhari Districts and Helmand Province) after they had been incapacitated by IED strikes. The Wisent, which was now available again, was also increasingly used, as the area of operations was considered to be highly IED-contaminated. A recovery tank was equipped with fascines to enable it to pass the numerous waterways in the AO. The Danish Leos made no enemy contact during this mission, which the commander of the tank with call sign 2, Oversergent Jonas, describes in Thomas Antonsen's book as the "Umbrella Effect." This effect refers to the already widely suspected assumption that the insurgents fled at the sight of battle tanks.

In August 2012, the rotation changed to DANCON 14. Premierløjtnant Nikolaj from the Jydske Dragonregiment took over the TANKDET. Kaptajn Martin served as a permanent liaison officer in the British battle group staff. For the first time, a complete replacement tank crew was available in Afghanistan, thus spreading the operational burden over more shoulders. In the course of DANCON 14, the operational activity of the TANKDET decreased more and more as the Afghan security authorities gradually took over responsibility.

On August 14, 2012, the new rotation participated for the first time in an operation, which took place east of Helmand near Girishk. Once again, the tanks were to monitor the infantry units' actions in the Green Zone from an elevated position. Since the marching route to the said position was considered IED-contaminated, the TANKDET was reinforced by a platoon of U.S. forces using a vehicle with radar-based mine detection capability. The TANKDET and the U.S.

91

unit reached the position above the Green Zone where the mine detection vehicle was struck by an IED while searching the area and became inoperative due to the detonation. The driver remained unharmed. After that, the Wisent of the Danes took over further demining. He drove up a slope consisting of loose sand. An IED hidden in a yellow plastic cup was released from the ground and rolled behind the Wisent. The Wisent was now trapped between a Leopard 2 positioned directly in front of it on a cliff edge and the IED. Dismounted pioneers of the TANKDET then began a search on foot for more nasty surprises. Their mine detectors made a warning sound so often that it was decided to request Explosive Ordnance Disposal help. However, the British battle group could not provide an EOD team until the following day, which meant that Danes and Americans had to stay on site. Due to the large number of suspected IEDs, the vehicles could only move in the existing ruts and were therefore extremely limited in their options. The next day, EOD forces arrived and freed the Wisent so that the TANKDET and the U.S. forces could continue their mission – with a 24-hour delay. Only the Leopard on the edge of the cliff had been in position from the beginning and was, therefore, able to oversee the Green Zone all along.

Between September 11 and 19, 2012, the Danish Leopards participated in an operation in an area called Yahkchal, east of the Helmand River. British and Afghan troops lined up to rid this area of insurgents. On the night of September 11, the TANKDET left MOB Price and drove along Highway 1 towards the target area. As the tanks left the runway for the rally point, the Leo with call sign 2 suffered damage to one of the road wheel arms in the middle of the desert. The damaged tank moved to Camp Bastion with an escort, the rest of the TANKDET continued to the rally point. At the southern end of Yahkchal, the tanks took up elevated positions near a waterway. British infantrymen advanced further south into the Green Zone along the waterway and moved into some buildings as bases. During patrols, they encountered insurgents several times.

At one of these enemy contacts, visibility conditions were deplorable due to sand particles in the air. The British had come under fire when they had left for the Green Zone. Nikolaj's gunner, after some searching, spotted wisps of smoke from fired RPGs. He then identified two insurgents with a Russian machine gun on the roof of a building only 300 meters from the British. Nikolaj's tank eliminated the targets with a multi-purpose round; the distance was estimated at 1,880 meters by the laser range finder. Probably because of the poor visibility conditions, the insurgents had not detected the Leopards because they had made no attempt to hide. The remaining fighters then fled. Upon completion of the operation in Yahkchal, the TANKDET returned to MOB Price.

From October 2012, the situation for the Danish tanks changed. They were increasingly guarding the dismantling and the closure of British bases, for example, in late October/early November 2012. The commander of 1st Battalion Scots Guard, Lieutenant Colonel Howieson, assesses the Danish Leopard's deployment as a successful deterrent in an e-mail to DANCON. Several attempts by the insurgents to launch an attack on the dismantling teams were identified, which were eventually not carried out due to the Danish Leopards' presence, which could be proofed by movement profiles of identified insurgents and their radio communication.

In the middle of February 2013, DANCON 15 took over, the command of the Danish tanks was assumed by Premierløjtnant Christian.

In June 2013, the Afghan security authorities took over responsibility for the entire country, and ISAF was assigned only a support role, which also changed the situation for the TANKDET. From then on, ISAF focused on counter-IED measures and the evacuation of casualties. The changed situation in the country ensured that the activities of the TANKDET declined noticeably. For example, the Danish Leos did not fire a single shot in anger during DANCON 15, which was probably also due to the now more narrowed down Rules of Engagement that left less room for military action. Nevertheless, Thomas Antonsen considers this to be primarily the result of successful deterrence.

The new rotation's first operation revolved around the dismantling of a British patrol base about one kilometer outside the Green Zone. Another goal was to attract the Taliban's attention to relieve U.S. forces north of the British battle group, which had recently been subjected to fierce attacks. The Danish tanks guarded the dismantling of the patrol base during this operation. On the night before the planned withdrawal, the insurgents were able to hide several IEDs along the routes the British would take to and from the patrol base to be dismantled, despite ISAF surveillance measures. Within a few hours, three British vehicles were blown up, bringing the entire column leaving the Patrol Base to a standstill. Premierløjtnant Christian decided to clear an alternative route with the Wisent, which took the next 14 hours. Starting at nightfall, ISAF artillery illuminated the area with illumination ammunition as bright as day. A Danish armored recovery vehicle towed one of the British vehicles to Price, and the British and Danes finally managed to clear the patrol base.

From May 2013 onwards, other patrol bases were dismantled, which usually involved a guarding assignment lasting several days for the TANKDET. Besides, preparations by the Danish Armed Forces to clear the FOB Price were in full swing. On July 22, the Danish tanks left the base as part of a large column and moved to their new base, Camp Bastion, and thus under the U.S. Task Force Belleau Wood wing. The Danish tank unit was given its own area of responsibility south-southwest of the camp, about 20 by 50 kilometers, to increase the presence of the task force there in order to keep the Taliban away from Bastion with spoiling attacks. As a rule, the tanks remained in the AOR for two to four days. Premier Løjtnant Christian was also granted extended rules of engagement again, which meant that he could again open fire on targets identified as hostile.

One of these operations was Operation Brutus in cooperation with the U.S. Marines. The operation had two objectives: Show of force in the AO and clarify the insurgents' whereabouts and strength. A Danish mobile electronic warfare team intercepted and analyzed numerous Taliban radio transmissions, and Danish tanks oversaw the Marines' advance. The Taliban avoided any confrontation.

A further major guarding assignment for the TANKDET was to carry out in June 2013. 3rd Brigade of the 215th Corps of the ANA led Operation Qalb, in which British and Danish troops participated. It took place in the Yakhchal region from June 20 to 24, 2013, with the Danish tanks once again shadow the progress of the other units.

Premierløjtnant Steffen led the TANKDET of DANCON 16 (August 2013 to February 2014) from 2nd Eskadron of the Jydske Dragonregiment. During this rotation, the Helmand Task Force was dissolved, and many bases used by the Danes were closed. During these projects, the TANKDET often guarded any dismantling and closure activities.

The first operation of significance occurred between September 9 and 12, 2013; the objective was to close Forward Operating Base Ouellette east of the Helmand River and approximately 60 kilometers from Camp Bastion. The Danish Leos were to provide external security for the dismantling of a section of the FOB. During this period, the problem was an ever-growing and increasingly aggressive crowd of young men who were probably eager to steal material from the construction site. They got into fights with the Afghan police and the British at the Forward Operating Base and eventually turned their attention to the Danish Leopards. Stones flew in the direction of the battle tanks, some even used slingshots. All warnings of the Danes fizzled out. Even directly firing a signal pistol at the crowd of young men had only short-term effects. Soon stones flew again against the Danish tanks. Although the Leopards confronted the crowd frontally and from one side, the young men were not deterred. Steffen finally fired some warning shots with his carbine, which made the crowd keep a distance of about 75 meters to the tanks. Nevertheless, the men continued to make the area unsafe.

The next day the game continued. The Danish tank soldiers also identified a man in the crowd who obviously had no interest in stealing construction materials but instead repeatedly spoke with a group of young men. The group soon disappeared behind a hilltop, where it was stirring up massive amounts of dust. Steffen let the Leo with call sign 3 carry out a change of position behind said hilltop. Thereby, the tank drove with the left track onto an anti-tank mine that detonated. Debris rained down on the tanks. The crowd fled in all directions. Pioneers and medics from FOB Ouellette then arrived, but all crew members of the struck tank were unharmed. The pioneers searched the area for more nasty surprises while the Wisent dragged the damaged Leo to the FOB. At 04:00 hrs the following night, a helicopter from Camp Bastion landed with spare parts and mechanics, and only 16 hours later, the crew of the struck tank was able to report readiness for action again.

After September 12, 2013, the TANKDET remained in Ouellette for another four days before returning to Bastion.

The last action for the tanks of DANCON 16 was an operation in cooperation with the U.S. Marines, who already suffered losses due to enemy snipers in the area of Patrol Base Boldak, about eight kilometers south of Camp Bastion. Thereupon they requested support from the Danes. The operation was called Leopard Shield 1. It served the purpose of driving the insurgents away from the vicinity of the patrol base. For this purpose, the Danish Leopards, divided into two groups, first took up positions in an elevated area south of Camp Bastion on January 23, 2014, from where they could oversee the actions of a U.S. Marine platoon. The platoon left Camp Bastion a little later. A few kilometers into the route, it was already under fire from handguns, whereupon the Marines sought cover in a building in a small village. The Danes then used a Puma UAV to identify about 10 Taliban hiding in a building at the other end of the same village. Marines' quick reaction force rushed in from Camp Bastion, but on the way, they came under RPG fire that resulted in heavy casualties. TANKDET commander Steffen and the tank with call sign 7 dashed at breakneck speed across the village to the Marines, who were pinned down, which ended the battle.

This Leopard 2 A5 was photographed in May 2014 and took part in the last patrol during DANCON 17. Shortly after the NATO ISAF mission was completed and the Danish Leopard 2 returned to Denmark (Copyright Danish Defence Command, Kim Vibe Michelsen)

On January 27, 2014, the Marines and Danish Leopards again advanced to the village, coming under fire from a sniper before he and an accomplice tried to leave by motorcycle. Premierløjtnant Steffen could neither confirm the men's identity on the motorcycle nor inform his tanks at first because his radio did not work until after several restarts. After the Marines had confirmed the men on the motorcycle as the snipers, Steffen gave the two other tanks the firing order. These eliminated the target at a distance of 2,170 meters.

Shortly after that, the last rotation change to DANCON 17 took place in February. The personnel was now provided by 2nd Eskadron of 1st Panserbataljon of the Jydske Dragonregiment. Premierløjtnant Martin took over command of the TANKDET. For DANCON 17, the closing down of FOBs was also the focus of attention. Besides, the Danish Leos participated in spoiling attacks against the Taliban and reconnaissance and surveillance operations. Their activities focused increasingly on the capabilities of their mobile electronic warfare team.

On April 25, 2014, the TANKDET participated in Operation Chainmail under British command. Two British infantry companies combed the area around Patrol Base Boldak. Once again, the Danish Leopards guarded the operation from an elevated area. As the tanks were about to retreat to their harbor for the night at about 17:15 hrs, the rearmost Leo of the column came under hand-gun fire. Tank commander Oversergent Mads reconnoitered two men on a motorcycle who moved at high speed towards some buildings in the Green Zone. He took up the pursuit but soon lost them. Mads was driving back to the harbor when two men briefly appeared between the buildings and presumably fired a Kalashnikov at his vehicle. When they showed themselves again around 17:40 hrs, Mads' gunner fought them off with a multi-purpose round. With this, the tank had fired the last shot in anger of Danish tanks in combat in the Hindu Kush. Recordings by a UAV confirmed that at least one of the two attackers was wounded.

Between May 1 and May 5, 2014, the TANKDET watched Highway 1, over which columns were moving from closing bases to Camp Bastion. From May 6 to 10, the Danish Leopards moved to FOB Sterga II south of Girishk to oversee this base's dismantling, with the tanks regularly patrolling along the supply roads to prevent IEDs from being placed there.

The TANKDET finally ceased its work in Helmand on 10 May 2014.

Leo 2 Tanks during the Coup d'état attempt in Turkey

The Bosphorus Bridge in Istanbul (which was renamed the 15 July Martyrs Bridge afterward) was closed by units of the renegade military during the night of the coup d'état attempt. Among other things, clashes with the population occurred after President Erdoğan called on them to resist. Pictures from the night and the day after prove that at least three Leopard 2 A4s were used on the bridge, although there is no evidence that the tanks used their armaments against those loyal to Erdoğan. Instead, the Leos appear to have been used as a show of force means and as mobile barriers. Photos from the day after show civilians who had climbed up the Leopard tanks and decorated them with Turkish flags.

Christiaan Triebert has evaluated the chat transcripts of high-ranking putschists from the coup night. They referred several times to own tanks near the bridge mentioned above and also outside Istanbul in the Sakarya Province and within reach of the city district Çamlıca. The chats' participants expressed concern about the government's call to resist the putschists and therefore considered how they could switch off the transmission towers in Çamlıca. The tanks within reach of the said city district were most likely the Leos on the Bosporus Bridge. It remains unclear which tank types were used in Sakarya.

Additional video footage from the night of the coup attempt also indicates that at least two other Leopards 2s were deployed in addition to the three tanks on the Bosporus Bridge. One video shows how two Leopard 2 A4 TUs drove onto a busy street on July 16 at around 01:50 hrs (the location is unknown). A man jumped in front of the first tank, hurled something at it twice, and then threw himself to the ground. The driver of the tank still braked but only came to a halt above the man. He then started up again and rolled on. The man, who was lucky not to have been hit by the tracks, immediately rose and caught the attention of a second Leopard 2, which was approaching. The tank did not attempt to stop. The man threw himself to the ground again, and the Leo rolled over him. Since the man was again not hit by the tracks, he survived another time. These two Leopards must have been different tanks than those on the Bosporus Bridge because that bridge was reportedly blocked by Leopard tanks between 22:00 and 23:00 hrs, and the photos from the next morning show that the tanks were still there. Against this background, it seems unrealistic to assume that they briefly left the bridge after midnight and returned later, so it can be suspected that at least five Leopard 2s were used in the course of the coup. Possibly the video could show the mentioned tanks in Sakarya.

Leopards under Turkish Flags in Syria

The Turkish Army used tank units equipped with Leopard 2s for both Operation Euphrates Shield and Operation Olive Branch.

From December 8, 2016, the Turkish military deployed up to 45 Leopard 2 tanks at al Bab, about 35 kilometers northeast of Aleppo. There is talk of at least 43 tanks arriving at al Bab between December 8 and 10, which means that an entire battalion is likely to be deployed. Photos indicate that the tanks were of the variant Leopard 2 A4 TU with hardly any visible modifications. Previously, the Turkish Armed Forces had already lost about a dozen of their outdated M60 battle tanks in the course of Operation Euphrates Shield. However, there are no indications of possible combat missions of the Leopard 1 within the scope of the operations described.

At that time, Al Bab was considered an IS stronghold. The terrorist fighters of the so-called Islamic State of Iraq and Syria (ISIS) had withdrawn after heavy fighting with the Free Syrian Army (FSA) forces and Turkish units. As a rule, infantry and technicals (cars converted for combat use) of the FSA push forward; the Turkish Armed Forces supported these attacks from the background. The FSA forces, some of which had been recruited from refugee camps in Turkey, were probably of low combat value, and there were language barriers between Turkish soldiers and FSA fighters. Since Turkey only supported the FSA offensive instead of fighting on the front line herself, it must be assumed that it did not call upon its army's full potential in Operation Euphrates Shield.

The Turkish Leopard 2 tanks were first brought to the deployment area by rail and given a new desert camouflage paint job on site. They possibly operated in platoons of three Leos each. The deployed unit was probably the 1st Battalion of the 2nd Armored Brigade. Only Christiaan Triebert is unsure whether the tanks were being assigned to the 1st or 2nd Armored Brigade. According to Mister Anàlisis, the Leopards were usually deployed in platoons, sometimes even individually. They were usually ordered to take up positions from where they could overlook the battlefield in order to provide fire support from these fixed positions, in consultation or not with the FSA, which fought at the front.

It is possible to reconstruct several combat situations of Turkish Leopard tanks which took place in the course of the al Bab offensive until December 15, 2016: On one occasion, the available footage confirms that one tank in a hull-down emplacement was hit by an anti-tank guided missile (ATGM) in the turret, possibly a US-produced TOW-2A. Mister Anàlisis assumes that the ATGM was a Russian model since ISIS probably hardly ever got its hands on TOW weapons. While Kurdish fighters of the YPG are likely to have used mainly TOW-2A anti-tank guided missiles, the ISIS equipped its troops with Russian 9K111 Fagots and 9M133 Komets. Also, AT-7 Metis and AT-5 Konkurs are said to have been used against Turkish Leopard 2s. The different sources also contradict each other in stating whether the missile penetrated the armoring in the described incident, but they agree that all crew members survived.

In another encounter, raiding parties armed with ATGMs sneaked up on at least two Turkish Leopards in hull-down positions between a slope and some buildings from behind the Turkish lines and fired at them from behind or from the side. First, a missile hit the turret of one Leo – it is unknown whether the hit penetrated the armor and what became of the crew. A second Leopard 2 located in the immediate vicinity did not react at all to this attack until another missile from behind hit it. The hit ignited either the hydraulics or the stored ammunition because visibly enormous flames sprang from the tank. Again there is no information about casualties among the affected crew.

Neither the footage nor descriptions by witnesses indicate that other service branches of the Turkish Armed Forces were involved in these two incidents, which raises the question of whether the Leos operated on their own at al Bab. Only a few photos of Operation Euphrates Shield show mechanized infantry combined with small Leopard units (maximum platoon-size). It is also striking that the hull-down positions during the described encounters only consisted of earth walls in front of the tanks; in the second incident, there was only a wall on one side that was too low to cover the whole panzer. Thus, the flanks of the Leos remained partly exposed, which brings up the question of whether there were no pioneers deployed who could have dug better firing positions for the tanks. It was precisely these uncovered flanks and rear that the enemy forces took advantage of in both encounters described.

December 16, 2016, finally marked a black day for the Turkish Armed Forces. In a joint offensive with the FSA, the Hill Jabal Aqeel in the west of al Bab was taken after brief skirmishes. The attempt to advance further west was fended off by ISIS. In a counterattack with vehicle-born IEDs, at least 16 Turkish soldiers were killed near Al Bab's hospital. ISIS itself claims even more than 70 Turkish soldiers were killed.

Triebert suspects that a total of more than 60 Turkish soldiers were killed in action by February 2017, most of them killed in the battle of al Bab. Besides, ISIS was able to capture two Leopard 2 A4 TUs during the fighting near the hospital, which the terrorists themselves prove by a video that was released on December 22, 2016. Mister Análisis was able to verify that Leopard 2 tanks were captured by ISIS in at least two other cases in a damaged condition (one had thrown the right track when it hit a mine or an IED) and were only later destroyed – possibly by ISIS itself to produce more compelling images for its propaganda. In one case, it was claimed in social media that a Leopard 2 had been loaded with a bomb that was then detonated from a distance by the shot of an M82A1 Barret. Obviously, Turkish recovery tanks were deployed in northern Syria. Still, they sometimes seemed unable to recover damaged Leopards in time – another indication that the tanks were operating primarily on their own.

In a longer propaganda video of ISIS of January 20, 2017, several destroyed Leopard 2 tanks are shown. Two of the tanks had their turret blown off, which indicates an internal explosion. Triebert concludes that the tanks were destroyed either by anti-tank guided missiles or even by a Turkish airstrike to prevent them from falling into the hands of the enemy (Mister Análisis suspects the latter due to the devastated wrecks). Two of the damaged Leopard 2s in the ISIS Video located west of al Bab were later recovered, presumably by Turkish forces or their allies.

At the end of the Battle of al Bab, the 2nd Armored Brigade had lost 10 Leos, as an inventory list of the Turkish Army shows leaked on December 23, 2016, on the Internet and is considered genuine. 5 panzers fell victim to anti-tank guided missiles, 2 were lost due to mines or IEDs, one due to artillery bombardment. The reason for the destruction of 2 is unknown according to the list (here, the suspicion arises that the Turkish military would prefer not to explain in black and white that they had to destroy their own tanks by an airstrike – in any case, the number fits like a glove). Christiaan Triebert confirmed that at least eight different Leopard 2s were destroyed by evaluating the existing photos of Leo wrecks in Syria. Turkish generals, therefore, described the Battles of al Bab as a trauma.

This Leopard 2 probably hit a mine or an IED, which smashed one track

The Turkish Air Force probably destroyed these two Leopard 2 A4s

The Turkish tank force was supplied with various ammunition types during Operation Euphrates Shield: KE rounds from Turkish production, APFSDS rounds from Israeli production, and HE and HEAT ammunition. One must assume that mainly HE and HEAT rounds were used if one looks at the weapon system inventory of ISIS and Kurdish militias. KE rounds could have been used mainly against vehicle-borne suicide bombers. This ammunition has a higher muzzle velocity and is therefore well suited to stop vehicles converted to bombs.

Christoph Roblin's analysis also deals with the deployment of Leos in al Bab. He concludes that they were used as long-range fire support batteries – in other words, quasi-static field guns – to guard the actions of Syrian militias and Turkish commandos at the front. For this purpose, the Leopard 2 tanks were deployed in highly visible (sometimes hull-down) positions, isolated from other troops. Yet again, Jeff Jager certifies that the Turkish Armed Forces made effective use of their forces in joint arms operations but only considers the period until about mid-October. At that time, Turkey had lost at least 9 M60 main battle tanks. Jager concludes that there is still potential for optimization at the tactical level in order to avoid such losses in the future.

Leopard 2s were also used in Operation Olive Branch. The tanks could have been retrofitted with reactive armor on the turret and Aselan Akkor active protection systems, which fire a kind of fragmentation charge at incoming missiles to neutralize them. There is no reliable information on whether these systems have been mounted on Leopards deployed in Syria.

Leopard 2 tanks fired on Kurdish positions near Afrin, with social media reports of several dozen civilians killed. The Kurdish side released a video on January 21, 2018, showing the attack on a Leopard tank, once again in a hull-down position, with a 9M113 Konkurs anti-tank guided missile. According to Gernot Kramper of Stern Magazine, the tank was only damaged in the attack.

A second video from February 3, 2018, is supposed to show the destruction of a Turkish Leopard 2 tank by a Konkurs ATGM, fired by Kurdish fighters. In fact, a battle tank-like vehicle can be seen at a great distance on the edge of a village, which disappears in a thick cloud of explosions and smoke after the ATGM's impact. The location is designated as Heftar near Afrin by the video description. It is noticeable that the tank-like vehicle does not move from the beginning of the recording until the impact of the ATGM (after all 50 seconds). The tank-like vehicle is located on the outskirts of the town on a road in an exposed position, but it is not alone. A vehicle that cannot be identified due to lousy video quality is located next to it, and further movement can be detected on or next to a building to the left. Whether the tank-like vehicle was a Leopard 2 cannot be conclusively determined from the footage. However, it is definitely a large tracked vehicle with a turret, which corresponds strongly to the Leo 2 in terms of shape – if one looks at the conflicting parties and their inventory, the vehicle depicted can almost exclusively be a Turkish main battle tank since the FSA, Kurdish militias and ISIS hardly or not at all have such vehicles at their disposal. Thus the probability of this being a Leopard 2 is very high.

References for this Chapter

In his book, Frank Lobitz (2009) discusses the international mission deployments of the Leopard 2; this also applies to the Netherlands' engagement in Bosnia. Compare Grummitt (2020) and Saunderson (1996) for further reading.

On KFOR, I would first like to refer you to Freundeskreis Panzerbaillone 203 204 213 e.V. It should be noted that it remains unclear whether the chronicle of PzBtl 214 speaks of the invasion of Kosovo, in which the unit undoubtedly participated, or of a later KFOR rotation. In any case, the information provided contradicts other sources about the invasion of Kosovo (for example, Eder speaks of only one reinforced mechanized battalion, not two battalions with one as the lead unit). Zwilling (2018b) and (2020) treats the German KFOR participation too, as well as Eder (2019), Lohse (undated, a), (undated, b), (undated, c), (undated, d), Radig (undated, a), (undated, b) and (undated, c), Flender (undated), Dreher (2019), Uffelmann (undated), Koelbl (2000), Kirchhoff (undated), Hauf (undated), Pfeil (2019), Tagesschau (1999) and Rhein-Zeitung (1999). Maloney (2019) is impressive concerning the background of KFOR and the difficulties in cooperation of the NATO states with Greece. He also discusses individual deployments of German Leopard 2s. Furthermore, YouTube is a rich source for the KFOR mission, namely Bundeswehr (2019), Egzon Dina (2015), and Sommer, A. (2009). Furthermore, the undated text of Apropos Kosovo is very intriguing, but at the same time should be treated with caution, as a clear political opinion underpins it and also makes the faux pas of calling the Leopard 2 a Fuchs tank. Therefore, I underline the core statements from Apropos Kosovo with another source: Köhler (2000). For further impressions of the German Army's invasion of Kosovo, see Elshanii Besart (2015), Spiegel TV (1999), as well as Deutscher BundeswehrVerband (2019a) and picture alliance (1999). Kriemann (2019) also mentions the invasion of German Leopard 2s into Kosovo in his treatise on the Kosovo war, as does Clement (2000). The events surrounding the murdered Stern Magazine reporters are discussed by Spiegel (1999). Plans for the scenario of an attack by Yugoslav troops on Kosovo are treated in Maloney (2019) and Reinhardt (2002). For Rudolf Scharping's assessment of the Leopard mission, see also Clement (2000). Harald Scheer (2011) also comments on the KFOR mission. Attention: This very source should be treated with great caution; therefore, see Linsler, C. & Kohlstruck, M. (2018): The SS in the cultural practice of German right-wing extremism (1990-2012). In: Schulte, J. & Wildt, M. (eds.): Die SS in der kulturellen Praxis des deutschen Rechtsextremismus (1990-2012). In: Schulte, J. & Wildt, M. (Ed.): Die SS nach 1945: Entschuldungsnarrative, populäre Mythen, europäische Erinnerungsdiskurse (Berichte und Studien, Band 76). 1st edition, V&R unipress.

For the episode in Tetovo, see Frankfurter Allgemeine (2001a), (2001b), (2001c) and Spiegel (2001) as well as Carl Schulze's online essay (2020). Essential Harvest is covered in NGO – Die Internet-Zeitung (2002) and NATO (2002).

Thomas Antonsen (2016) is to be consulted on the deployment of Danish Leopards in Afghanistan, also Curry (2006) and Schulze (2011). P. Dueholm (2010) gives an overview of the Danish engagement in Afghanistan. The Frankfurter Allgemeine Zeitung article on the incident of February 26, 2008, can be found in Lohse (2008).

On the deployment of Canadian Leopard 2s for ISAF, see Walter Hålands (2012) article in the Austrian magazine TRUPPENDIENST, Allan Joyner (2019), Trevor Cadieu (2008), Schulze (2010a), (2010b) and (2015) as well as Canadian American Strategic Review (undated) and Defense Industry Daily (2014) offer insights too. The fight for Mushan is discussed in Maloney (2009). For details about the letter of thanks to the Federal Ministry of Defense, see Florian Flade (2010).

The attempted coup d'état in Turkey is treated by Heinrich (2016), Tagesschau (2016), The Telegraph (2016), and Triebert (2016).

The deployment of Leo 2s under the Turkish flag is discussed by Patrick Truffer (2017), m.m. (2016), Aboufadel (2016), Kramper (2018), Jager (2016), Roblin (2019), Triebert (2017), Mister Análisis (2017) and FOCUS (undated). The term trauma for the Battle of al Bab can be found at Gebauer & Schult (2018). For the video of February 3, 2018, see Steinmeier (2018).

It should be mentioned that Truffer is wrong in his assertion that there were no losses of Leopard 2 tanks in either Kosovo or Afghanistan. The FOCUS also misrepresents this. All in all, it must be noted that the source situation regarding the deployment of Turkish Leos in Syria is extraordinarily uncertain and is based on private blogs and news reports. An in-depth analysis of the primary sources is missing and cannot be provided in this book.

Conclusion

Before I come to my conclusion, I would like to make it clear that I differentiate between missions within the framework of the UN and NATO on the one hand and operations under the Turkish flag on the other. Furthermore, I would like to mention that there were undoubtedly more combat situations with Leopard tanks involved in the context of the conflicts described, which are either not documented or whose documentation is not accessible. However, there should not have been any extraordinary incidents not covered by this very book because such cases would certainly have produced press articles.

First of all, I look at the lessons learned that can be derived from missions in the context of UN and NATO missions: Both Leopard panzer models were initially designed for tank duels in Central Europe. Focusing on this scenario will undoubtedly lead to shortcomings as soon as another scenario arises. Both Leopards are, for example, only conditionally suitable for subtropical and tropical climate zones due to a lack of air conditioning. Still, at the same time, they prove to be convertible. In his paper "Leopard Tanks and the Deadly Dilemmas of the Canadian Mission to Afghanistan" (2007), the political scientist Michael Wallace, who was a critic of the Canadian decision to deploy main battle tanks at the Hindu Kush at the time, warned of the risks of using tanks from the 1960s in a modern warfare scenario. However, his concerns were not to come true.

Due to the constant development of both tank models, they are able to meet modern warfare requirements (this holds true especially for the Leopard 2, for the Leopard 1, it holds true in a limited manner), but the problem areas must be kept in mind. For example, the intercom fails due to the heat generated in the fighting compartment, as happened with the Leopard 1 in Afghanistan, which can lead to an awful outcome in a worst-case scenario. However, the various combat missions prove that specifically, the Leopard 2 in its more recent variants is particularly suitable for modern military missions.

Cadieu's assertion that deploying main battle tanks reduces collateral damage among the civilian population and infrastructure is noteworthy. In his view, tanks can be used more precisely against enemy forces than indirect fire, namely artillery and airstrikes. The latter is a popular military instrument in modern warfare and peacekeeping operations. Think of Kosovo, where dozens of civilian casualties were caused by NATO airstrikes. Or think of the NATO mission in Libya in 2011. It seems that airstrikes are easier for decision-makers to order because they are supposedly less risky (for their people).

On the other hand, the main battle tank always comes with the psychological element of an instrument of a war of aggression; a nation that uses such weapons of war may fear being considered a warmonger. This may also be one of the reasons why Western countries are very reluctant to deploy battle tanks. One shuns the negative press, which is highlighted by the discussions in Canada, Germany, and Denmark that accompanied main battle tanks' deployment. Both Leopard tank models are precision tools demonstrated not least by their operations under the Danish and Canadian flags in the Hindu Kush, where they opened fire on insurgents in numerous situations without harming friendlies, civilians, or the infrastructure in the immediate vicinity. It is not for nothing that Thomas Antonsen coined the term "65-tonne sniper rifle" for the Leopard 2 tank in his book (Antonsen, T., 2016, p. 115). Windsor et al. also speak at one point of the Leo 1 as a "massive "sniper rifle" (Windsor, L. et al., 2008, p. 165). Also, Rugarber should be mentioned again, whose explanations support this assertion. In any case, there is a lot of evidence for Cadieu's hypothesis in the combat operations described in this book. For example, the Danish tank operation north of Forward Operating Base Sandford on November 24, 2007, proves how precisely the Leopard 2 can engage the enemy without causing collateral damage. In addition, not a single deployment of Leopard tanks has been documented in which innocent people were harmed.

Western states' tendency to use indirect fire in military conflict situations seems almost absurd before this evaluation. Negative press is also caused by the fact that, for example, NATO is bombing a train full of refugees in Kosovo, or that their own soldiers are killed in Afghanistan because the vehicle in which they were sitting was blown to pieces by an explosive device. The deployment of battle tanks significantly reduces the probability of both of these scenarios. Or as Major Cadieu puts it in simple terms: "Leopard C2 tanks have saved Canadian and Afghan lives. (Cadieu, T., 2008, p. 21). Against the background of these findings, the question indeed arises as to why other states did not also conclude that they should deploy battle tanks in Afghanistan in order to protect the lives of their own soldiers better – yes, I'm looking at you, dear German Federal Ministry of Defence!

Both Leopard models' user states are generally very reluctant to deploy battle tanks. 13 armed forces procured the Leopard 1, 19 even the Leopard 2. Although many of the user states have been involved in a wide variety of military conflicts and abroad missions since the procurement of their Leopards, they have only very rarely made use of their German panzers. One example is the Canadian Armed Forces, which refrained from using battle tanks both in the Second Gulf War and in the attack on the Taliban regime (Operation Enduring Freedom), even though the Iraqi Armed Forces, for example, had tanks at their disposal themselves. Instead, the Canadian Armed Forces at that time came up with the idea of being able to do without battle tanks altogether. It is remarkable that the Leopard 1, which was developed for tank duels of a hot Cold War, ultimately proved its value and the value of its arm of the service in an asymmetric war against insurgents who themselves had no battle tanks. Thus the Leo 1 contributed to a change of course by the Canadian military in the tank question. Major Cadieu consequently considers the deployment of the Leopard 1 tanks in the Hindu Kush to be decisive in the struggle for power over the Kandahar Province. Leopard 1s and Leopard 2s enabled the Canadian ISAF forces to overcome rugged terrains that would otherwise have remained impassable and attack and seize fortified enemy positions.

Also, the protection factor cannot be estimated highly enough. Overall, not a single Canadian tanker was killed in action in Afghanistan, although the Leopards were involved in numerous battles and struck by many IEDs. The Leopard 2 A6M CAN, which was already equipped with a special mine protection package during its development and was later upgraded with enhanced mine protection, probably saved the lives of many Canadians, or to put it another way: If the Canadian Armed Forces had refrained from using their Leopards in the Hindu Kush, they would probably have suffered more casualties and badly wounded overall, because the IEDs would then have hit LAV III infantry fighting vehicles, Bison armored personnel carriers or even M1028 Strykers – in all these vehicles the occupants are much worse protected against explosions than in Leopard 1 and Leopard 2 main battle tanks.

If we look beyond Canada, it is clear that the same can be said for other armed forces and other threats: The Danish soldiers would probably not have survived the quadruple mine explosion in Bosnia more or less unscathed in any other vehicle of the Danish Armed Forces. And even if the Royal Danish Army in Afghanistan has one tanker KIA among its Leopard crews, this does not contradict the general hypothesis when considering that the Danish tankers had fought for seven years straight in the Hindu Kush.

Besides, the various Leo operations include a wide variety of combat situations that would have been much more dangerous for own and allied troops without the deployment of battle tanks – for example, the incident with the IED factory east of Girishk.

In Afghanistan, the Leos played an essential role in breaking the Taliban's power in Kandahar. The insurgents had no battle tanks themselves, and IEDs, mines, and RPGs are no sure-fire means of defeating Leopard tanks. Consequently, once a Taliban commander had a significant, virtually insoluble problem ahead of him if a Leopard appeared in his sector – not to mention the psychological effect Ralf Raths describes in a catchy way during his appearance in the Literarischer Salon. Reports about the fear of simple Taliban fighters of Leopard tanks are numerous and partly proven by studies. Oversergent Jonas called this fear and the resulting lack of attacks "Umbrella Effect."

That this deterrence works effectively is demonstrated impressively by the various operations Leopard tanks conducted. There were no major attacks on KFOR forces in Kosovo, most of which rolled into the country with battle tanks. The German Armed Forces had to use the armaments of their tanks rarely. And for Afghanistan, there are many indications that the presence of Leopard tanks prevented many insurgent attacks and quickly resolved numerous combat situations in favor of the ISAF forces with little to no loss. Moreover, the guarding of other units' actions by Leopard tanks can be considered effective and contributes to protecting the participating forces at the front. The Turkish example shows that it is just as important to secure the guarding tanks themselves adequately.

It can also be assumed that the Canadian and Danish operations in Afghanistan would have been less successful without the use of Leopards and that the Taliban's power position would therefore have eroded less, which in turn would have made further attacks on ISAF troops more likely. In this respect (admittedly, with many subjunctives), the Leos thus contributed to the protection of ISAF personnel.

As a first interim conclusion, therefore, can be noted: The use of Leopard tanks provides considerable protection for one's own troops as well as for allies, both through the protection that the vehicles offer their occupants and through the protection that they provide through fire support and deterrence.

This conclusion is supported, among other things, by the contemporary assessments of Lieutenant-Colonel Lavoie and Brigadier General Fraser under the impression of Operation Medusa, where it was shown that neither the envisaged M1028 Strykers nor the bulldozers equipped with improvised armoring could replace a battle tank on the battlefield. The conclusion is further shared by the retrospective observations of Major Cadieu and other actors in Afghanistan and the Balkans, as presented in the various chapters. This interim conclusion is apparently contradicted by Överste Peter Lundberg (Sørensen, K., 2020, p. 122), the Swedish battalion commander during Operation Amanda in 1994. Lundberg says that the deployment of the Danish tanks in Bosnia instead intensified the enemy fire. However, this also happened under a less than robust mandate with very narrow rules of engagement. In general, the UNPROFOR mission illustrates the extent to which the Leopard tanks' effectiveness is hampered when the leadership gives the tank soldiers hardly any options for action. The recurrent shelling of UN troops certainly did not come to an end because the Bosnian Serb forces did not have to fear any consequences. In any case, it is obvious that attacks on Danish Leopards ceased the moment they were given extended rules of engagement by the NATO mission IFOR. This finding further supports the interim conclusion without refuting Lundberg. It emphasizes the importance of a robust military mandate for the effectiveness of the protection factor.

For Kosovo, it can be stated that the decision for mechanized forces in the form of, among other things, Leopard 2s may have contributed to the fact that the Serbian Armed Forces firstly behaved peacefully during the invasion, and secondly that Milošević later refrained from a renewed attack on the NATO-occupied country. NATO considered both scenarios as quite conceivable, but the sight of columns of battle tanks and other mechanized forces may have brutally demonstrated to the Serbs their inferiority. In any case, it can be said that due to the tensions in the country between refugees, Kosovo Albanians, other minorities, and the UÇK on the one hand, and the soldiers and special police forces of Miloševićs on the other, it was anything but self-evident that the withdrawal of the Serbs would take place mainly without violent excesses. Therefore, I will propose the hypothesis that the presence of modern, impressive Leopard battle tanks encouraged all conflicting parties to hold themselves back. Incidents such as the one in Prizren on June 13 would possibly have occurred more frequently without NATO MBTs in the country and possibly would have inflicted losses on all sides. Even if this must remain a hypothesis I cannot prove, it has its charm. It should encourage people to reconsider Western states' general reluctance to deploy battle tanks in foreign missions. Andrew Leslie, who took command of the 1st Canadian Mechanized Brigade Group in 1997, once said this: "If you see a bunch of confident, professional-looking soldiers with up-to-date equipment rumbling around in tanks or Coyotes or APCs, they will project an aura of ability to do what has to be done and guess what? The local bad guys won't do anything." (Maloney, S., 2019, pos. 2172 in the Kindle edition).

However, battle tanks, specifically the Leopard 1 or 2, should not be seen as a panacea for military missions. The Taliban found quite effective means in Afghanistan with homemade explosives and mines to slow down NATO tanks and even end a Danish Leo driver's life. These experiences make it clear that Leopards should never operate isolated but within the framework of combined arms, even against an enemy without any large equipment at his disposal. On its own, even a Leopard 2 of the most modern variant is helpless in many situations. Danes, Canadians, and Germans have deployed their tanks properly and were able to minimize their losses – of course, no military effort is free of risk.

Cadieu also points out that modern armed forces must ensure strategic global air transport capabilities in their own right to be able to react quickly to changing situations and be independent of third parties. The Canadian example of the mission in Kosovo, in particular, shows the dangers of outsourcing necessary military competencies to private sector companies or cutting secondary military competencies. The main battle tank cannot be reduced to its firepower, protection, and mobility but must also be integrated into a functioning supply and logistics system. The best main battle tank in the world is of little use if its army lacks the means to move it to the area of operations or to supply it with spare parts and ammunition on site. Based in particular on the Canadian experiences, but also on the Bundeswehr's experiences with damages to its vehicles in Macedonia by standing still, it should therefore be concluded that special attention must be paid to the logistics behind every MBT deployment. The KFOR mission, in particular, demonstrates the importance of the ability to transfer troops worldwide quickly and purposefully using the Bundeswehr's resources. In any case, the imagination of Canadian war material being at the mercy of some Ukrainian ship crew for a month-long journey is scary. However, what the Danes in Bosnia, for example, and NATO troops in general in Greece, underwent also make it clear that the concept of logistics must be understood in a broader sense: political and bureaucratic systems from the home country to the country of deployment must also be considered and dealt with. Denmark's KFOR participation indicates that private-sector solutions can work well too.

Another lesson learned from the KFOR mission is that the spatial separation between the large equipment in Krivolak and the crews in Tetovo, 150 kilometers away, must be avoided in future scenarios. The said separation meant that the troops had only limited opportunities to perform technical service on their vehicles. Furthermore, securing them against sabotage was problematic. Moreover, the troops could have spent the agonizing phase of waiting in Macedonia carrying out field exercises if they had had their equipment with them. The then Major Radig, member of the vstk MechBtl's staff, goes even further in his assessment of these circumstances: "we acted naively and were lucky." (Radig, P., undated, c, p. 241, own translation). The picture of the unkempt tank, from whose barrel the plants proliferated, as Werner Pfeil draws it, is symbolic of the problem of a separate storage area for the weapon systems.

In Afghanistan in particular, ensuring the combat readiness of tanks operating simultaneously in different parts of the province posed a major challenge. It remained a bottleneck in the activities of the Danish and Canadian Leopards. The episode surrounding the two Leopard 1 C2s, which fell out in June 2007 as reinforcements of an infantry company on its way to the area of operations, illustrates the risks associated with the fragmentation of one's tank force. On their own, the two Leos and the infantrymen could not recover the tanks and therefore had to wait for help in a dangerously exposed position. Had they operated within the framework of an entire tank squadron, additional vehicles would have been available for recovery tasks.

Both Leopard models are rated as powerful machines with low maintenance needs, among others by Sørensen. For example, experiences with the Leopard 2 during Operation Moshtarak also show that it is an extremely reliable main battle tank that can be operated autonomously for long periods.

Furthermore, the doctrine of modern tank deployment in asymmetric warfare must be addressed. Gone seem to be the days when a battalion was the smallest possible tank unit. In Afghanistan, it was often necessary to further split the few Leopard forces in order to reinforce individual infantry units or columns with more firepower and protection. For its own protection, the tank must never operate alone but always in combined arms.

Cadieu considers the allocation of command between the tank commander for the attack phase and the infantry commander for the consolidation phase for some Canadian operations in 2007 to be expedient, even if this meant that the command would change back and forth times in the course of action. Also, he emphasizes the importance of comprehensive training, which must range from the training of individual soldiers to country of deployment-specific training and combined arms exercises.

Have the numerous Leopard 2 tanks destroyed in the course of the Turkish military offensives between 2016 and 2018 now revealed the weaknesses of this model, as manifold media reports stress? And do those destroyed Leos provide the counterevidence for my above mentioned hypothesizes?

First of all, I must state that the Leopard 2 A4 variant used at al Bab is considered obsolete by today's standards. Besides, the Turkish unfavorably deployed their tanks. In more or less good hull-down positions, they were just waiting to be fired at instead of taking advantage of their mobility. In the incident in mid-December 2016, in which two Leos were hit by ATGMs one after the other, the crew of the second tank showed no reaction to the hit on the first tank – they should have got on the move immediately. So there is indeed evidence that Turkey was not making optimum use of its tanks, as some experts accuse it of doing. The combat incidents described and the footage that exists of them also raise the question of the role of Turkish tanks in combined arms operations. Thus it seems as if the Turkish Leos are left instead of being reinforced by troops. To support this argument, the deployment of Danish and Canadian Leos in Afghanistan should be taken into consideration. Both nations used this type of tank for years in the fight against insurgents, Canada sometimes even Leopard 2 A4s (but upgraded to Leopard 2 A4 CAN). And although the insurgents of Afghanistan were equipped with anti-tank weapons comparable to those of ISIS and the Kurdish fighters (RPGs, 82-millimeter recoilless guns, mines, IEDs), in seven years of continuous combat operations, "only" a single tank was destroyed, and a single tanker soldier was killed.

The Leopard 2 A4 variant was designed for tank duels of the Cold War with clear weak points in the side, rear, and turret armor. However, in northern Syria, it encountered a situation in which the Turkish Armed Forces faced a partly asymmetrically fighting enemy. Only later upgrades of the Leo paid tribute to this form of warfare. Nevertheless, even the 2 A4 variant proves its high protection factor. If, for example, a Konkurs missile hits a modern main battle tank from the side or the rear, it will cause even greater damage when no special defensive measures such as slat armor are mounted. The intelligent design of the Leopard 2, including a fire extinguishing system, ammunition placed in a separate compartment, and more, had probably prevented worse in northern Syria.

Turkey's strategy, which was not advantageous for the deployment of battle tanks, is possibly due to the fact that Ankara wanted to limit its involvement in northern Syria and therefore sent only supporters for the FSA front troops instead of a fully equipped offensive battle group. As a result, Leopards provided fire support on their own, rather than working together with Turkish pioneers, infantrymen, and other forces. The Leopard 2, however, was never designed to be a static field gun.

However, it should be noted that the fighting in northern Syria has significantly scratched at least the nimbus of Leo 2's invincibility. The press reports are now in the world, and they also do not differentiate between the different variants and do not take into account the underlying tank doctrine. It makes a considerable difference whether a Leopard 2 A4 is used as a static field gun or a Leopard 2 A7V in a combined arms operation.

However, if we look at the actual losses of German, Canadian and Danish Leopards, a completely different picture emerges after about 20 years of combat missions in the Balkans and Afghanistan:

For the Leopard 1, it is to conclude that there were no total losses at all. Even the heaviest explosions like the mine accident in Bosnia in January 1996 were not able to destroy this tank. The struck Leo could be repaired and was later used in other operations. In Leopard 1 missions, at least one tanker was wounded in Bosnia and six in Afghanistan.

What about the Leopard 2? With it, the Danes suffered one dead and one tank as a total loss, in addition to at least four wounded. The Canadian Leopard crews have at least five wounded and no total loss of tanks. Given the many years of numerous operations up to the limits of human and material, these findings speak strongly for the Leopard tanks and contradict the Turkish loss figures. Ten Leopard 2s were probably lost in December 2018, and numerous Turkish tankers may have been killed or wounded in the process.

I hope this book contributes to the assessment of the Leopard tank family, which puts the battle tank in general and the Leopard models in particular in a different light. These weapon systems are by no means idols of offensive warfare. Here, Goebbel's propaganda echoes, in particular, taken up and reinforced by modern pop culture. To substantiate this argument, I would like to refer to recent Eastern European war flicks, which are essentially about bombastic tank action, such as "T-34" or "White Tiger," and features large material battles.

Decision-makers should not misunderstand the Leopard tanks in politics and the military as mere conventional warfare instruments. A public debate on the deployment of battle tanks in foreign missions must be endured if necessary, like the Canadians, Danes, and, in the case of KFOR, even the Germans have demonstrated. At the end of the day, after analyzing all the combat operations of these three nations, I can conclude that the decision to send Leopard 1 and Leopard 2 tanks to Bosnia, Kosovo, Macedonia, and Afghanistan...

1. ...protected own troops. Attacks did not take place at all because of the deterrence factor, or the Leopards contributed in case of attacks because the survival chances of the own troop increased considerably. A robust military mandate is decisive for the effectiveness of protection by the use of Leopard tanks.

2. ...prevented collateral damage since modern battle tanks are precision instruments.

3. ...casualties among tankers and total losses of main battle tanks were kept extraordinarily low because the Leopards were used in combined arms operations according to modern operational doctrines.

Against these findings' background, the user states should urgently consider their Leopard 1 and 2 main battle tanks for current and future military missions if the threat situation is corresponding. So the German Federal Ministry of Defence may turn its attention to Mali...

106

Postscript by Thomas Antonsen

The two German Main Battle Tanks, the Leopard 1 and the Leopard 2 are two very different vehicles, yet they have the same historical point of origin, the Cold War between NATO and the Warsaw Pact, which ended in 1989 without ever erupting into open war. Both vehicles were built to counter the massive armoured threat from the Warsaw Pact, which had a constant quantitative superiority and an ever decreasing qualitative gap compared to the NATO partners throughout the entire period.

All armoured vehicles are constructed within the three parameters of armour, mobility and firepower. This was true in 1917 when the first tank-like vehicle entered service with the British Army, and it will also be true for whatever vehicle will replace the Leopard 2.

The Leopard 1 was built as relatively light (40 ton class), with focus on firepower and mobility, and thus its lack of armour was less important, as mobility was seen as the factor which could compensate for the lack of heavy armour. When the Leopard 1 entered service with the German Army in 1965, it was equipped with the British L7A3 105 mm gun, which quickly became a NATO standard tank gun. Together, the gun and the very manoeuvrable platform ensured that the Leopard 1 became a very popular vehicle in NATO and abroad, which is still used and has been continuously been upgraded throughout its service life. Many Leopard 1 users has switched to the Leopard 2, yet in 2006 the Canadian Army deployed 15 of its Leopard 1C2 to Afghanistan. Here they served in a direct fire support role, providing Canadian and other NATO partners with swift and accurate fire support, until first accompanied by and later replaced by a Canadian version of the Leopard 2.

The Leopard 2 tank entered service with the German Army (Bundeswehr) in 1979, and at the time it seemed like its constructors had finally managed to circumvent the three principles mentioned above. It was a 60 ton vehicle, with state of the art firepower through its 120mm Rheinmetall gun, and at the same time unrivalled mobility with its 1500 hp MTU engine. How was this possible? Well, the armour was and is based on layered or composite technology, rather than the solid "Rolled Homogenous Armour" which had been the norm before composite armour was introduced in the Leopard 2, and soon after in the American Abrams and the British Challenger tank. Throughout its years in service, the Leopard 2 has been gaining weight, and its mobility has to some degree suffered, since it still has the 1500 hp engine. The Leopard 2 will be in service with the German Army and many other NATO partners until at least 2035. It is safe to say, the vehicle has been an outstanding success since its introduction. User nations range from Norway in the North, to Chile in the South, Canada in the West and Singapore and Indonesia in the East. More users are currently taking the Leopard 2 tank into service, and all the users have a strong incentive to continue to keep the Leopard 2 tank a viable weapons platform, able to counter whatever threats the Leopard 2 will meet in the future. The key to its success is, and has always been that it is a platform, which can be adapted to the various threats, which it encounters. The Danish Army continued to adapt the vehicle to the threats posed by the Taliban insurgents during the years 2007-2014 when the Leopard 2 protected infantry from the Danish and other NATO armies in Afghanistan. Also it should be noted, that no vehicle is impervious to attack. The Canadians and the Danes learned that in Afghanistan and the Turks learned that on the border to Syria. In all the instances mentioned above, it was proved time and again, that the quality of the crew, or the lack of crew quality, it the key to success or failure. Currently, the German and Danish armies and the armies of other user nations take the Leopard 2A7 into service, and this 3rd generation of the Leopard 2 is in many respects a new vehicle build inside the upgraded hulls of previous versions of the Leopard 2. Should tensions between NATO and Russia in erupt into open hostilities, for instance the Baltic states, it will for the next many years be the Leopard 2A7 which will stop whatever armoured vehicles Russia will use in such a conflict.

All in all, the Leopard 2 has been an outstanding success since its introduction with the German Army in 1979. When it will be replaced by another type of MBT around 2035-2040, it has been in service for 60+ years, and no other similar vehicle can boast of this feat.

About the Author, Jill Marc Münstermann

I was born on 25 November 1988 in Tönisvorst. In 2008 I joined the Bundeswehr as a sergeant candidate. I completed my basic and full training in Schwarzenborn with Jägerregiment 1 (= Light Infantry Regiment 1), followed by training courses throughout Germany, before I became a member of the German Army Aviation in 2010 and was posted to Wesel with Fernmeldebataillon 284 (= Signal Battalion 284) and later with 1st NATO Signal Battalion as an instructor for recruits as well as to conduct political education and mission preparation training. Further training courses followed in Bückeburg and Münster, where I was finally promoted to Feldwebel (= sergeant). At another seminar in Stetten am kalten Markt in the Bundeswehr's Center for Explosive Ordnance Disposal, I attended training in detecting and reporting booby traps and unexploded ordnances. Since 2012 I worked mainly in the administration of the 1st NATO Signal Battalion and organized events within the barracks' public relations.

In the summer of 2014, I left the army. I started as an apprentice at the German bank Targobank. At the same time, I started studying alongside my apprenticeship. I completed my apprenticeship as a dialog marketing specialist in 2016 and my Bachelor of Arts degree in International Business and Social Sciences in 2019.

Since October 2018, I have been responsible as Operations Manager for the on-call medical service of the Kassenärztliche Vereinigungen (= Associations of Physicians) of North Rhine-Westphalia and Westphalia-Lippe.

At the same time, I have been appearing as a fictional literature writer under various pseudonyms since 2014. Since 2018 I have also been working as an editor and publisher. For this purpose, we have founded EK-2 Publishing GmbH.

I am married, have two children, and live with my family in North Rhine-Westphalia. Since summer 2020, I am (again) a member of the Verband der Reservisten der Deutschen Bundeswehr (= Association of Reservists of the German Armed Forces). Also, since that year, I am a member of a political party represented in the Bundestag.

Acknowledgment

I want to thank Jochen Vollert of TANKOGRAD PUBLISHING – Verlag Jochen Vollert for his advice on his house's publications on the Leopard tank family. I would like to warmly recommend the high-quality publications from his house to all interested readers. I would also like to thank Thomas Antonsen, he enriched my book with photos and his expertise and wrote a substantial postscript.

I would also like to thank my wife and my two children, who inspired my writing and borrowed me to my laptop for many hours.

Events

I will be happy to provide extracts/ insights from this book in readings, lectures, or discussions. Please address your request via e-mail directly to me.

jill.muenstermann@ek2-publishing.com

Feedback

I hope I got everything right, especially English military terms. Nevertheless, have you noticed any mistakes? Do you have knowledge of further missions of the Leopard tanks? Do not hesitate to write to me. I will gladly consider new knowledge for later editions and am always grateful if I can expand my horizon.

jill.muenstermann@ek2-publishing.com

Sources List

21ˢᵗ Century Asian Arms Race (2018): Spanish Leopard 2 Tanks Are Getting A Minor Upgrade. Link: https://21stcenturyasianarmsrace.com/2018/09/20/spanish-Leopard-2-tanks-are-getting-a-minor-upgrade/ [accessed July 31, 2020]

Aboufadel, L. (2016): Turkish Army offensive takes disastrous turn in east Aleppo as slain soldiers litter battlefield. In: AMN Al Masdar News. Link: https://www.almasdarnews.com/article/turkish-army-offensive-takes-disastrous-turn-east-aleppo-slain-soldiers-litter-battlefield/ [accessed October 10, 2020]

Althaus, J. (2019): Der Leopard 2 war seinem US-Gegenstück deutlich überlegen. Link: www.welt.de/geschichte/article204290414/Panzer-Der-Leopard-2-ist-so-gut-dass-er-55-Jahre-im-Dienst-bleibt.html [accessed July 6, 2020]

Antonsen, T. (2016): Danish Leopards in Helmand. 1. edition, Trackpad Publishing

Apropos Kosovo: 1999 – 2014: Der Einsatz der Bundeswehr im Kosovo. Link: http://reporterreisen.com/apropos-kosovo/iframes/bundeswehr.html [accessed July 24, 2020]

Army Guide (undated): Leopard 1. Link: http://www.army-guide.com/eng/product152.html [accessed June 20, 2020]

Army Vehicles (undated): Leopard 1 Family. Link: https://www.armyvehicles.dk/Leopard1a3.htm [accessed June 9, 2020]

Aziz, S. (2017): TSK SURİYE'DE NEREYE GİDİYOR?-1. Link: https://belluminexpertis.wordpress.com/2017/02/15/tsk-suriyede-nereye-gidiyor-1/ [accessed August 2, 2020]

Bockenheimer, J. & Simantke, E. (2015): Panzer in der Schuldenkrise. Link: https://www.tagesspiegel.de/wirtschaft/ruestungsexporte-nach-griechenland-panzer-in-der-schuldenkrise/11722550.html [accessed August 2, 2020]

Brewster, M. (2007): Germany gets thank-you note from Canadian IED survivor. Link: http://milnewstbay.pbworks.com/f/ThankYouToDEU-CP-Canoe-052039Dec07.pdf [accessed June 9, 2020]

Bromley, M. & Guevara, I. (2014) [erstmals veröffentlicht 2010]: Arms modernization in Latin America. In: Tan, A. (Ed.): The Global Arms Trade – A Handbook. 1. Edition, Routledge.

Bron Pancerna (2015): Belgian Leopard 1A5BE. Link: https://www.flickr.com/photos/bronpancerna/22411092156/ [accessed September 27, 2020]

Bundesministerium der Verteidigung (2018): Europäische Rüstung stärken. Link: https://www.bmvg.de/de/aktuelles/europaeische-ruestung-staerken-25498 [accessed June 9, 2020]

Bundesregierung (2013): Rüstungsexporte – Verkauf von deutschen Leopard-Kampfpanzern an Staaten des Mittleren Ostens und an weitere Länder. In: Deutscher Bundestag. Link: https://www.waffenexporte.org/wp-content/uploads/2013/04/KA-R%C3%BCstungsexporte-Leopard-Kampfpanzer-11.9.13.pdf [accessed August 2, 2020]

Bundeswehr (2019) [Erstausstrahlung vermutlich 1999]: Classix: Einmarsch der Bodentruppen zur KFOR-Mission (1999) – Bundeswehr. Auf: Youtube. Link: https://www.youtube.com/watch?v=I4PIlf8qrm8 [accessed Juli 23, 2020]

Bundeszentrale für politische Bildung (2012): Deutsche Panzerlieferungen. Link: https://sicherheitspolitik.bpb.de/m5/articles/german-tank-exports [accessed June 23, 2020]

Bundeszentrale für politische Bildung (2017): Vor 25 Jahren: UN-Sicherheitsrat beschließt Friedensmission UNPROFOR für Kroatien und Bosnien-Herzegowina. Link: https://www.bpb.de/politik/hintergrund-aktuell/242979/1992-unprofor-mission [accessed June 25, 2020]

Cadieu, T. (2008): Canadian Armour in Afghanistan. In: Canadian Army Journal Vol. 10.4, Canadian Army Publishing CFB Kingston

Calic, M. (2017): Kleine Geschichte Jugoslawiens. In: Bundeszentrale für politische Bildung. Link: https://www.bpb.de/apuz/256921/kleine-geschichte-jugoslawiens?p=3 [accessed June 25, 2020]

Canadian American Strategic Review (undated): Hard Numbers – CF Afghanistan Casualties by Vehicle Type. Link: http://web.archive.org/web/20080116190726/http://www.sfu.ca/casr/ft-vehicle-casualties-2.htm [accessed August 6, 2020]

Citino, R. (2010): Death of the Wehrmacht: The German Campaigns of 1942. Link: https://www.youtube.com/watch?v=UNDhswF1GKk&t=2803s [accessed June 9, 2020]

Clement, R. (2000): Die Teilnahme der Bundeswehr am internationalen Militäreinsatz im Kosovo und in Jugoslawien. In: Reiter, E. (Ed.): Der Krieg um das Kosovo 1998/1999. V. Hase & Koehler Verlag

Curry, B. (2006): Canada beefs up Afghan war commitment. Link: https://www.theglobeandmail.com/news/national/canada-beefs-up-afghan-war-commitment/article1103544/ [accessed June 26, 2020]

Dan (2019): Mehr große Raubkatzen für Europa. In: Spartanat. Link: https://www.spartanat.com/2019/11/mehr-grosse-raubkatzen-fuer-europa/ [accessed June 31, 2020]

Dederichs, M. (2001): Vor 50 Jahren – Soldaten der belgischen Armee kommen nach Altenrath. In: Zeitschrift für Mitglieder und Freunde des Heimat- und Geschichtsvereins Troisdorf e.V., Nr. 25. Link: http://geschichtsverein-troisdorf.de/wp-content/uploads/2019/08/hug-nr.-25-juni-2001.pdf [accessed September 27, 2020]

Defence Industry Daily: Tanks for the Lesson: Leopards, too, for Canada. Link: https://www.defenseindustrydaily.com/tanks-for-the-lesson-Leopards-too-for-canada-03208/ [accessed November 14, 2020]

Defence Turkey (2010): The last Leopard-1 Tank modernized by ASELSAN. Volume 4, Issue 20. Link: https://www.defenceturkey.com/en/content/the-last-Leopard-1-tank-modernized-by-aselsan-413 [accessed June 26, 2020]

Defence Turkey (2011): Aselsan's Leopard 2 Upgrade Solution. Volume 5, Issue 27. Link: https://www.defenceturkey.com/en/content/aselsan-8217-s-Leopard-2-upgrade-solution-600 [accessed August 2, 2020]

Der Bundesrat (2006): Das Rüstungsprogramm 2006. Link: https://www.admin.ch/gov/de/start/dokumentation/medienmitteilungen.msg-id-5352.html [accessed July 30, 2020]

Der Bundesrat (2010): Verkauf von überzähligen Leopard-2-Kampfpanzern an den deutschen Hersteller. Link: https://www.admin.ch/gov/de/start/dokumentation/medienmitteilungen.msg-id-36295.html [accessed July 30, 2020]

Deutscher BundeswehrVerband (2019a): Vor 20 Jahren: Der Kfor-Einsatz der Bundeswehr beginnt. Link: https://www.dbwv.de/aktuelle-themen/blickpunkt/beitrag/news/vor-20-jahren-der-kfor-einsatz-der-bundeswehr-beginnt/ [accessed July 24, 2020]

Deutscher BundeswehrVerband (2019b): 40 Jahre Leopard 2 – Stärke auf Ketten. Link: https://www.dbwv.de/aktuelle-themen/blickpunkt/beitrag/news/40-jahre-Leopard-2-staerke-auf-ketten/ [accessed June 9, 2020]

Dreher, F. (2019): Falko Dreher, Oberstleutnant. In: Eder, M. (als Ed., 2019) [first published in 2000]: Dienen für den Frieden im Kosovo. Neuedition, HePeLo Verlag Golbet

Dueholm, P. (2010): Denmark in Afghanistan. Link: http://www.netpublikationer.dk/um/10526/pdf/denmark_in_afghanistan.pdf [accessed June 26, 2020]

Eder, M. (als Ed., 2019) [first published in 2000]: Dienen für den Frieden im Kosovo. Neuedition, HePeLo Verlag Golbet

Eder, M. (1999): Weisung Nr. 1 für den Einsatz KFOR. In: Eder, M. (als Ed., 2019) [first published in 2000]: Dienen für den Frieden im Kosovo. Neuedition, HePeLo Verlag Golbet

Egzon Dina (2015) [footage from 1999]: KOSOVË: PRIZREN: TRUPAT GJERMANE TË NATO-s VRASIN DY SNAJPERIST SERBË. Auf: Youtube. Link: https://www.youtube.com/watch?v=i904UcFp9Ck [accessed July 24, 2020]

Elshanii Besart (2015) [footage from 1999]: Prizren13 Qershor 1999: Diskutim i tensionuar mes Kforit dhe Ushtris Jugosllave. Auf: Youtube.com. Link: https://www.youtube.com/watch?v=C4USPAU3yEc [accessed July 24, 2020]

Ernst, Wolfgang (2001): War Hitler ein Feldherr?: Der Oberste Befehlshaber der Wehrmacht im Zweiten Weltkrieg. Ohne Edition, Books on Demand

Esercito (2019): Combat Vehicles. Link: http://www.esercito.difesa.it/en/Equipment/Combat-Tanks-and-Armoured-Vehicles/Combat-Vehicles [accessed June 22, 2020]

Feichtinger, W. (2000). Die militärstrategische und operative Entwicklung im Konfliktverlauf. In: Reiter, E. (Ed.): Der Krieg um das Kosovo 1998/1999. V. Hase & Koehler Verlag

Finlayson, K. (2008): OPERATION BAAZ TSUKA: Task Force 31 Returns to the Panjwayi. In: Office of the Command Historian. Link: https://arsof-history.org/articles/v4n1_op_baaz_tsuka_page_2.html [accessed October 31, 2020]

Fischer, M. (2017): Bosnien-Herzegowina. In: Bundeszentrale für politische Bildung Link: https://www.bpb.de/internationales/weltweit/innerstaatliche-konflikte/54780/bosnien-herzegowina [accessed June 25, 2020]

Flade, Florian (2010): Im "Leopard" bombensicher durch Afghanistan. In: Welt. Link: https://www.welt.de/politik/deutschland/article7214428/Im-Leopard-bombensicher-durch-Afghanistan.html [accessed October 17, 2020]

Flender, E. (undated): Die 2./ vstkMechKp in Prizren / an der Grenze. In: Eder, M. (als Ed., 2019) [erstmals veröffentlicht 2000]: Dienen für den Frieden im Kosovo. Neuedition, HePeLo Verlag Golbet

FOCUS (undated): Er galt als unzerstörbar: In Syrien wird ein Panzer-Mythos zerstört. Link: https://www.focus.de/politik/videos/schwachstelle-entdeckt-verluste-in-syrien-ein-deutscher-panzer-mythos-wird-jetzt-zerstoert_id_6487678.html [accessed August 5, 2020]

Frankenfeld, T. (2009): Barack Obamas riskanter Kurs. In: Hamburger Abendblatt. Link https://www.abendblatt.de/politik/ausland/article108517513/Barack-Obamas-riskanter-Kurs.html [accessed August 5, 2020]

Frankfurter Allgemeine (2001a): Mehr Panzer, weniger Soldaten in Tetovo. Link: https://www.faz.net/aktuell/politik/mazedonien-mehr-panzer-weniger-soldaten-in-tetovo-117106.html [accessed July 21, 2020]

Frankfurter Allgemeine (2001b): Zwei Kompanien kommen aus dem Kosovo. Link: https://www.faz.net/aktuell/politik/bundeswehr-kontingent-zwei-kompanien-kommen-aus-dem-kosovo-130445.html [accessed Juliy 22, 2020]

Frankfurter Allgemeine (2001c): Deutscher Mazedonien-Kommandeur Harder: „Wir gehen mit großem Rückhalt in die Mission". Link: https://www.faz.net/aktuell/politik/faz-net-exklusiv-deutscher-mazedonien-kommandeur-harder-wir-gehen-mit-grossem-rueckhalt-in-die-mission-131911.html [accessed July 22, 2020]

Frankfurter Allgemeine (2018): Auf Eis gelegt: Türkische Leopard-2-Panzer werden nicht nachgerüstet. Link: https://www.faz.net/aktuell/politik/inland/tuerkische-Leopard-2-panzer-werden-vorerst-nicht-nachgeruestet-15416659.html [accessed November 3, 2020]

112

Franklin, S. (2018): A farewell to the Leopard 1 main battle tank. Link: https://canadianarmytoday.com/a-farewell-to-the-Leopard-1-main-battle-tank/ [accessed June 22, 2020]

Freundeskreis Panzerbaillone 203 204 213 e.V.: Das Panzerbataillon im KFOR Einsatz. Link: https://www.panzerbataillone-augustdorf.de/214-kfor/ [accessed July 23, 2020]

Galland, A. (2012) [first published in 1953]: Die Ersten und die Letzten – Jagdflieger im Zweiten Weltkrieg. 1. Edition, Verlagshaus Würzburg – Flechsig

Gebauer, M. & Schult, C. (2018): Berlin Weighs Tank Deal with Turkey to Free Journalist. In: Spiegel International. Link: https://www.spiegel.de/international/germany/arms-for-hostage-germany-explores-yuecel-deal-with-turkey-a-1189197.html [accessed October 18, 2020]

Global Security (undated): Turkish Army Equipment. Link: https://www.globalsecurity.org/military/world/europe/tu-army-equipment.htm [accessed June 23, 2020]

Gottschlich, Jürgen (2016): Das Militär, die AKP und der gescheiterte Putsch. In: Bundeszentrale für politische Bildung. Link: https://www.bpb.de/internationales/europa/tuerkei/233343/putschversuch-im-juli-2016 [accessed October 19, 2020]

Government of Canada (2018a): Kosovo Force (KFOR). Link: https://www.canada.ca/en/department-national-defence/services/military-history/history-heritage/past-operations/europe/kinetic.html [accessed August 16, 2020]

Government of Canada (2018b): Operation DETERMINED EFFORT. Link: https://www.canada.ca/en/department-national-defence/services/military-history/history-heritage/past-operations/europe/cobra.html [accessed August 24, 2020]

Gürbey, G. (2014): Der Kurdenkonflikt. In: Bundeszentrale für politische Bildung. Link: https://www.bpb.de/internationales/europa/tuerkei/185907/der-kurdenkonflikt [accessed October 19, 2020]

Grässlin, J. (2013): Schwarzbuch Waffenhandel – Wie Deutschland am Krieg verdient. Wilhelm Heyne Verlag

Greek Military Photos (undated): Leopard-1 in the Hellenic Army. Link: http://greekmilitary.net/greekmbtanks.htm [accessed June 23, 2020]

Grummitt, D. (2020): Leopard 2: NATO's First Line of Defence, 1979–2020. Tankcraft – Pen and Sword Military

Guderian, H. (1994) [first published in 1951]: Erinnerungen eines Soldaten. 18. Edition, Motorbuch-Verlag

Håland, W. (2012): Neue Herausforderungen für Kampfpanzer. In: TRUPPENDIENST, Issue 4/2012. Link: https://www.bundesheer.at/truppendienst/ausgaben/artikel.php?id=1421 [accessed June 26, 2020]

Hamburger Abendblatt (2013): Vertrag mit Deutschland über Kauf von 120 Panzern. Link: https://www.abendblatt.de/politik/ausland/article122182670/Vertrag-mit-Deutschland-ueber-Kauf-von-120-Panzern.html [accessed July 25, 2020]

Hauf, M. (undated): Vom Einsatz / Auftrag her denken!! Dies sollte vor allem im Bereich Personalwesen gelten! In: Eder, M. (als Ed., 2019) [first published in 2000]: Dienen für den Frieden im Kosovo. Neuedition, HePeLo Verlag Golbet

Hansen, O. (undated): Operation "Hooligan-Bashing" – Danish Tanks at War. Link: https://web.archive.org/web/20140221230137/http://www.milhist.dk/post45/boellebank/boellebank_uk.htm [accessed September 2, 2020]

Hähnlein, R. (2018): Militärisch unlösbar. In: Bundeszentrale für politische Bildung. Link: https://www.bpb.de/internationales/europa/tuerkei/257585/militaerisch-unloesbar [accessed June 26, 2020]

Hauser, G. (2008): Die NATO – Transformation, Aufgaben, Ziele. Peter Lang – Internationaler Verlag der Wissenschaften

Heiming, G. (2018): Leopard 2 und PzH 2000 für Ungarn. In: Europäische Sicherheit & Technik. Link: https://esut.de/2018/12/meldungen/land/9608/Leopard-2-und-pzh-2000-fuer-ungarn/ [accessed Juli 25, 2020]

Heiming, G. (2020): Modernisierung der polnischen Leopard 2 stockt. In: Europäische Sicherheit & Technik. Link: https://esut.de/2020/05/meldungen/20446/modernisierung-der-polnischen-leopard-2-panzer-stockt/ [accessed November 16, 2020]

Heinrich, D. (2016): Der Putsch und seine Helden. In: Deutschlandfunk. Link: https://www.deutschlandfunk.de/tuerkische-medien-der-putsch-und-seine-helden.1773.de.html?dram:article_id=361280 [accessed October 19, 2020]

Henken, L. (undated): Vom Tiger zum Leopard: Waffenexporte und Rüstungsindustrie in Kassel. In: Kasseler Friedensforum. Link: https://www.kasseler-friedensforum.de/280/rheinmetall/Vom-Tiger-zum-Leopard-Waffenexporte-und-Ruestungsindustrie-in-Kassel/ [accessed July 25, 2020]

Hilmes, R. (2006): 50 Jahre Fahrzeuge der gepanzerten Kampftruppen. In: Das schwarze Barett, Nr. 34, Freundeskreis Offiziere der Panzertruppe e.V.

Hilmes, R. (2011): KPz Leopard 1 1956-2003 – Typenkompass. 1 Edition, Motorbuch Verlag

Hilmes, R. (2016): 1916-2016 – Vom Tank zum Leopard 2. Link: https://www.youtube.com/watch?v=kWb-hH_MxiY&t=1279s [accessed June 9, 2020]

HNA (2016): Panzerbauer haben gut zu tun: KMW baut Leoparden und Pumas. Link: https://www.hna.de/kassel/rothenditmold-ort131614/panzerbauer-haben-tun-baut-Leoparden-und-pumas-panzerhaubitzen-6065986.html [accessed August 2, 2020]

Hodge, C. (2004): The Failure of Europe – Power and Irresponsibility. In: Nolan, C. (Ed.): Power and Responsibility in World Affairs – Reformation vs. Transformation, Praeger Publishers

Horn, B (2010): No Lack of Courage – Operation Medusa, Afghanistan. Dundurn

Hull, I. (2004): Absolute Destruction: Military Culture and the Practices of War in Imperial Germany. 1. Edition, Cornell University Press

Human Rights Watch (1995): Weapons Transfers and Violations of the Laws of War in Turkey. Link: https://www.refworld.org/docid/3ae6a7ea4.html [accessed August 30, 2020]

Ingvorsen, E. (2018): 44 kampvogne skal moderniseres: Koster mindst 829 millioner mere end forventet. In: DR Nyheder. Link: https://www.dr.dk/nyheder/politik/44-kampvogne-skal-moderniseres-koster-mindst-829-millioner-mere-end-forventet [accessed August 1, 2020]

Jacobsen, H. (2014): Leopard 1 har skutt sin siste granat. Link: https://www.tv2.no/a/3592319 [accessed June 17, 2020]

Jager, J. (2016): Turkey's Operation Euphrates Shield: An Exemplar of Joint Combined Arms Maneuver. In: Small Wars Journal. Link: https://smallwarsjournal.com/jrnl/art/turkey%e2%80%99s-operation-euphrates-shield-an-exemplar-of-joint-combined-arms-maneuver [accessed October 19, 2020]

Joyner, A. (2019): The Leopard changes (some) of its spots. In: Canadian Army Today. Link: https://canadianarmytoday.com/the-Leopard-changes-some-of-its-spots/ [accessed August 6, 2020]

Kirchhoff, S. (undated): Mosaiksteine aus dem KVM und Kosovo-Einsatz 1999. In: Eder, M. (als Ed., 2019) [first published in 2000]: Dienen für den Frieden im Kosovo. Neuedition, HePeLo Verlag Golbet

Koelbl, S. (2000): "Der Kampf, das ist das Äußerste". In: Der Spiegel, Volume 6/2000

Kohl, M. (2019): Heavy Metal – Neuer Leopard rollt vom Band. Link: https://www.bundeswehr.de/de/organisation/heer/aktuelles/heavy-metal-neuer-Leopard-rollt-vom-band-146788 [accessed July 19, 2020]

Köhler, O. (2000): Auf erkannten Feind Feuer frei! In: Der Freitag – die Wochenzeitung. Link: https://www.freitag.de/autoren/der-freitag/auf-erkannten-feind-feuer-frei [accessed Juli 24, 2020]

Kramper, G. (2018): Wie dieser Leopard-Panzer einen Raketentreffer überlebte. In: Stern. Link: https://www.stern.de/digital/technik/wie-dieser-Leopard-2a4-einen-raketentreffer-ueberlebte-7831818.html [accessed October 19, 2020]

Krapke, P. (1986): Leopard 2: Sein Werden und seine Leistung. 1. Edition, Verlag E.S. Mittler & Sohn

Krauss-Maffei Wegmann (undated, a): Leopard 1 A5. Link: https://www.kmweg.de/systeme-produkte/kettenfahrzeuge/kampfpanzer/Leopard-1-a5/ [accessed October 31, 2020]

Krauss-Maffei Wegmann (undated, b): Die Varianten des Kampfpanzers LEOPARD. Link: https://www.kmweg.de/systeme-produkte/kettenfahrzeuge/kampfpanzer/ [accessed July 25, 2020]

Krauss-Maffei Wegmann (undated, c): Die Leistungsmerkmale des LEOPARD 2 A7+. Link: https://www.kmweg.de/systeme-produkte/kettenfahrzeuge/kampfpanzer/Leopard-2-a7/ [accessed July 25, 2020]

Krauss-Maffei Wegmann (undated, d): Performance characteristics of the LEOPARD 2 A4M. Link: https://www.kmweg.com/systems-products/tracked-vehicles/main-battle-tank/Leopard-2-a4/ [accessed August 6, 2020]

Kriemann, H. (2019): Der Kosovokrieg 1999. 2. Edition, Reclam Verlag

Kröning, A. (2016): Wie sich #TankMan vor den Leopard-Panzer warf. In Welt. Link: https://www.welt.de/politik/ausland/article157177346/Wie-sich-TankMan-vor-den-Leopard-Panzer-warf.html [accessed November 15, 2020]

Kurschinski, K. (2014): From Centurion to Leopard 1A2 by Frank Maas. In: Laurier Centre for Military, Strategic and Disarmament Studies. Link: http://canadianmilitaryhistory.ca/from-centurion-to-Leopard-1a2-by-frank-maas/ [accessed October 28, 2020]

Leopard Club (undated): LW016 - Belgian Leopard 1A5BE. Link: http://Leopardclub.ca/workshop/LW016/ [accessed September 27, 2020]

Lobitz, F. (2009): Kampfpanzer Leopard 2 – Internationaler Einsatz und Varianten. Verlag Jochen Vollert – Tankograd

Lohse, E. (2008): Leopardenjagd am Hindukusch. In: Frankfurter Allgemeine. Link: https://www.faz.net/aktuell/politik/ausland/afghanistan-Leopardenjagd-am-hindukusch-1513570.html [accessed October 15, 2020]

Lohse, J. (undated, a): Sammelraum Petrovec. In: Eder, M. (als Ed., 2019) [first published in 2000]: Dienen für den Frieden im Kosovo. Neuedition, HePeLo Verlag Golbet

Lohse, J. (undated, b): Die 4./vstkMechBtl im Sammelraum Petrovec. In: Eder, M. (als Ed., 2019) [first published in 2000]: Dienen für den Frieden im Kosovo. Neuedition, HePeLo Verlag Golbet

Lohse, J. (undated, c): Leben auf / neben / unter / in dem Panzer. In: Eder, M. (als Ed., 2019) [first published in 2000]: Dienen für den Frieden im Kosovo. Neuedition, HePeLo Verlag Golbet

Lohse, J. (undated, d): Die 4./PzBtl 33 erhält den Einsatzbefehl. In: Eder, M. (als Ed., 2019) [first published in 2000]: Dienen für den Frieden im Kosovo. Neuedition, HePeLo Verlag Golbet

Lüdeke, A. (2008): Panzer der Wehrmacht Band 1: 1933-1945. 1. Edition, Motorbuch Verlag

m.m. (2016): Leopard 2 in Syria. In: Below The Turret Ring. Link: https://below-the-turret-ring.blogspot.com/2016/12/Leopard-2-in-syria.html [accessed August 2, 2020]

Maloney, S. (2009): Panjwayi Alamo The Defence of Strongpoint Mushan. In: Canadian Military History, Volume 18, Issue 3

Maloney, S. (2019): Operation Kinetic – Stabalizing Kosovo. Potomac Books (University of Nebraska)

Malyasov, D. (2015): Photo of upgrade Leopard 2NG by by Aselsan of Turkey. In: Defence Blog. Link: https://defence-blog.com/news/army/photo-of-upgrade-Leopard-2ng-by-by-aselsan-of-turkey.html [accessed August 2, 2020]

Marcus, Aliza (2007): Blood and Belief: The PKK and the Kurdish Fight for Independence, NYU Press

114

Max (2016): KMW soll 88 Kampfpanzer Leopard 2 modernisieren. In: Hartpunkt. Link: https://www.hartpunkt.de/kmw-soll-88-kampfpanzer-Leopard-2-modernisieren/ [accessed June 22, 2020]

Max (2018). Modernisierung von Leopard 2 wird verschoben. In: Hartpunkt. Link: https://www.hartpunkt.de/modernisierung-von-Leopard-2-wird-verschoben/ [accessed August 1, 2020]

McPhedran, I (2007): Leopard tanks up for grabs. Link: https://www.heraldsun.com.au/news/victoria/tanks-to-scare-neighbours/news-story/3bdbecbe0b099412cc004e94159d68ce [accessed June 22, 2020]

Mister Análisis (2017): Achtung Leopards in Syria! Full analysis of the Leopard 2A4TR in Syria. Link: https://misterxanlisis.wordpress.com/2017/03/12/achtung-Leopards-in-syria-full-analysis-of-the-Leopard-2a4tr-in-syria/ [accessed October 21, 2020]

Mitteldeutscher Rundfunk (2020): Erste Leopard-Panzer an Ungarn ausgeliefert. Link: https://www.mdr.de/nachrichten/politik/ausland/erste-Leopard-panzer-fuer-ungarn-100.html [accessed July 25, 2020]

Nachtwei, W. (2019): Entschlossen + besonnen: Die Gratwanderung des 1. KFOR-Kontingents im Kosovo 1999 – Bericht mit Reden (unter anderem meiner) vom Ehemaligentreffen in Regen/Bayer. Wald. Link: http://nachtwei.de/index.php?module=articles&func=display&aid=1599&theme=print [accessed July 24, 2020]

Nasr, N. (2014): Stridsvagnar kör sista varvet. In: Sydsvenskan. Link: https://web.archive.org/web/20140718231258/http://www.sydsvenskan.se/skane/stridsvagnar-kor-sista-varvet/ [accessed July 30, 2020]

NATO (2002): Operation Essential Harvest (Taskforce Harvest). Link: https://www.nato.int/fyrom/tfh/home.htm [accessed July 21, 2020]

NATO (2006): Operation Baaz Tsuka secures two regions. Link: https://www.nato.int/isaf/docu/pressreleases/2006/pr061220-382.htm [accessed August 7, 2020]

Neitzel, S. (2018): In: "Schicksalsgemeinschaft – Europas Zukunft hundert Jahre nach dem ersten Weltkriegsende" – Aussage aus Diskussionsrunde. Link: https://www.youtube.com/watch?v=kyoHrKFb3OI&t=3100s [accessed June 17, 2020]

NGO – Die Internet-Zeitung (2002): Bundeswehr Mazedonien Rückblende. Link: https://www.ngo-online.de/2019/09/04/bundeswehr-mazedonien/ [accessed July 21, 2020]

NurW (2016): Indonesian Army Awaiting Arrival of Leopard RI Main Battle Tanks. In: Defense Studies. Link: http://defense-studies.blogspot.com/2016/05/indonesian-army-awaiting-arrival-of.html [accessed July 25, 2020]

Parsons, Z. (2006): My Tank is Fight! Citadel Press

Pauli, F. (2010): Wehrmachtsoffiziere in der Bundeswehr – Das kriegsgediente Offizierskorps der Bundeswehr und die Innere Führung 1955-1970. Ferdinand Schöningh

Pfeil, W. (2019): Ein Sommertag im Krieg – Mein D-Day im Kosovo. Lau-Verlag und Handel KG

picture alliance (1999): Verladung von Panzern für Kosovo. Auf: GettyImages. Link: https://www.gettyimages.de/detail/nachrichtenfoto/ein-sch%C3%BCtzenpanzer-vom-typ-marder-der-bundeswehr-rollt-nachrichtenfoto/1213184168 [accessed November 16, 2020]

Poehle, S. (2014): Das Ende der langen ISAF-Mission. Link: https://www.dw.com/de/das-ende-der-langen-isaf-mission/a-18142863 [accessed June 26, 2020]

Pöhlmann, M. (2016): Der Panzer und die Mechanisierung des Krieges – Eine Deutsche Geschichte 1890 bis 1945. Ferdinand Schöningh

Radig, P. (undated, a): Der Marsch in das Einsatzland. In: Eder, M. (als Ed., 2019) [first published in 2000]: Dienen für den Frieden im Kosovo. Neuedition, HePeLo Verlag Golbet

Radig, P. (undated, b): Prizren – eine Stadt im Chaos. In: Eder, M. (als Ed., 2019) [first published in 2000]: Dienen für den Frieden im Kosovo. Neuedition, HePeLo Verlag Golbet

Radig, P. (undated, c): 20 Jahre KFOR-Einsatz – Nachwirkungen aus der persönlichen Erinnerung. In: Eder, M. (als Ed., 2019) [erstmals veröffentlicht 2000]: Dienen für den Frieden im Kosovo. Neuedition, HePeLo Verlag Golbet

Railly News (2020): BMC to Modernize 84 Leopard 2A4 Tanks. Link: https://www.raillynews.com/2020/05/bmc-to-modernize-84-Leopard-2a4-tanks/ [accessed August 2, 2020]

Raths, R. (2020a): Panzer im Literarischen Salon – ein Abend zum Nachhören. Link: https://www.youtube.com/watch?v=jag-LZK3YqU [accessed July 2, 2020]

Raths, R. (2020b): Buchbesprechung "Der Panzer und die Mechanisierung des Krieges". Link: https://www.youtube.com/watch?v=4Gtd7AR6Nd8&t=1382s [accessed June 15, 2020]

Reinhardt, K. (2002): KFOR – Streitkräfte für den Frieden – Tagebuchaufzeichnungen als Deutscher Kommandeur im Kosovo. 2. Edition, Verlag der Universitätsbuchhandlung Blazek und Bergmann seit 1891

Reiter, E. (Ed.) (2000): Der Krieg um das Kosovo 1998/1999. V. Hase & Koehler Verlag

Rheinmetall Defence (2013): Indonesien bestellt militärische Kettenfahrzeuge bei Rheinmetall – Auftragsvolumen rund 216 MioEUR. Link: https://www.rheinmetall-defence.com/de/rheinmetall_defence/public_relations/news/archiv/archive2016/index~1_4480.php [accessed July 25, 2020]

Rheinmetall Defence (2017): Rheinmetall gewinnt bedeutenden Munitions-Rahmenvertrag der Bundeswehr. Link: https://www.rheinmetall-defence.com/de/rheinmetall_defence/public_relations/news/archiv/2017/aktuellesdetailansicht_7_14336.php [accessed July 18, 2020]

Rheinmetall Group (2016): Rheinmetall bringt 128 polnische Leopard 2-Kampfpanzer auf den neuesten Stand. Link: https://www.rheinmetall.com/de/rheinmetall_ag/press/news/archiv/archive2016/index_7424.php [accessed July 25, 2020]

Rhein-Zeitung (1999): … KFOR setzt Einmarsch fort. Link: http://archiv.rhein-zeitung.de/on/99/06/13/topnews/kfor.html [accessed August 11, 2020]

Roblin, S. (2019): Germany's Leopard 2 Tank in Syria Was Beaten Badly in Battle. Why? In: The National Interest. Link: https://nationalinterest.org/blog/buzz/germany%E2%80%99s-Leopard-2-tank-syria-was-beaten-badly-battle-why-78441 [accessed October 18, 2020]

Rugarber, J. (2011): Operation Cooperation and the Needs for Tanks. In: ARMOR – Mounted Maneuver Journal, Issue January-February 2011, U.S. Army Armor School

Ruttig, T. (2017): Afghanistan. In: Bundeszentrale für politische Bildung. Link: https://www.bpb.de/internationales/weltweit/innerstaatliche-konflikte/155323/afghanistan [accessed June 26, 2020]

Saunderson, J. (1996): 18th January 1996 During the war in Bosnia: a Dutch Leopard II Main Battle Tank being unloaded from a ship in the Croatian port of Split. Link: https://www.alamy.com/18th-january-1996-during-the-war-in-bosnia-a-dutch-Leopard-ii-main-battle-tank-being-unloaded-from-a-ship-in-the-croatian-port-of-split-image378703441.html [accessed November 6, 2020]

Schack, G. (1926): Die Heereskavallerie im Zukunftskriege. In: Deutsche Wehr; Beilage: Das Wissen vom Kriege, Nr. 3

Scheer, H. (2011): "Leopard" am Hindukusch. In: Nummer 81, Deutsche Militärzeitschrift – Achtung: Diese Quelle ist mit großer Vorsicht zu genießen, siehe dazu unter anderem: Linsler, C. & Kohlstruck, M. (2018): Die SS in der kulturellen Praxis des deutschen Rechtsextremismus (1990-2012). In: Schulte, J. & Wildt, M. (Ed.): Die SS nach 1945: Entschuldungsnarrative, populäre Mythen, europäische Erinnerungsdiskurse (Berichte und Studien, Volume 76). 1. Edition, V&R unipress

Schulze, C. (2010a): Canadian LEOPARD 2A6M CAN. Verlag Jochen Vollert – Tankograd

Schulze, C. (2010b): Taskforce Kandahar. Verlag Jochen Vollert – Tankograd

Schulze, C. (2011): DANCON-ISAF: DANISH BATTLEGROUP. Verlag Jochen Vollert – Tankograd

Schulze, C. (2015): Leopard 2A4M CAN. Verlag Jochen Vollert – Tankograd

Schulze, C. (2020): Bundeswehr Leopard MBT at 40. Link: https://www.joint-forces.com/features/31652-bundeswehr-Leopard-2-mbt-at-40-part-6 [accessed July 22, 2020]

Seidl, C. (2018): Bundesheer muss seine verbliebenen Panzer nachrüsten. In: Der Standard. Link: https://www.derstandard.at/story/2000084423074/bundesheer-muss-seine-verbliebenen-panzer-nachruesten [accessed August 1, 2020]

SFOR Stabilization Force (undated): Historyof the NATO-led Stabilisation Force (SFOR) in Bosnia and Herzegovina. Gehört zum offiziellen Webauftritt der NATO. Link: https://www.nato.int/sfor/docu/d981116a.htm [accessed July 27, 2020]

Shepard (2019): Finnish Leopard 2A6 fleet complete. Link: https://www.shephardmedia.com/news/landwarfareintl/finnish-Leopard-2a6-fleet-complete/ [accessed August 1, 2020]

Smit, W (2014): Dutch Leopard 1: Armoured Fist of the Dutch Army. 1. Edition, Trackpad Publishing

Sommer, A. (2009): Bundeswehr In Aktion News!!! Video. Auf: Youtube. Link: https://www.youtube.com/watch?v=61twNAFM1No [accessed July 24, 2020]

Sørensen, K. (2020): The Leopard 1 in Danish Service. Trackpad Publishing

Spiegel (1992): "Keine Kontrolle mehr". Link: https://www.spiegel.de/spiegel/print/d-13683197.html [accessed June 26, 2020]

Spiegel (1994): Furchtbar präsent. Link: https://www.spiegel.de/spiegel/print/d-13682487.html [accessed June 26, 2020]

Spiegel (1996): "Leo" in Reserve. Link: https://www.spiegel.de/spiegel/print/d-9133461.html [accessed June 9, 2020]

Spiegel (1999): "Einfach verdammtes Pech". Link: https://www.spiegel.de/spiegel/print/d-13850110.html [accessed August 11, 2020]

Spiegel (2001): Deutsche Panzer in Tetovo. Link: https://www.spiegel.de/politik/ausland/mazedonien-deutsche-panzer-in-tetovo-a-123195.html [accessed June 21, 2020]

Spiegel TV (1999): Kosovo Krieg

Spielberger, W. (1995): Waffensysteme Leopard 1 und Leopard 2. 1. Edition, Motorbuch-Verlag

Steinmeier, G. (2018): Direct ATGM hit: Kurdish female fighters destroy invading Turkish Leopard 2 tank in Afrin region. Auf: Youtube. Link: https://www.youtube.com/watch?v=YafzmkvVRiI [accessed June 12, 2020]

Stragey Page (2009): Armor: Aging Leopards Prowl the Andes. Link: https://www.strategypage.com/htmw/htarm/articles/20090116.aspx [accessed June 12, 2020]

Tagesschau (1999): Tagesschau vom 12. Juni 1999, ARD

Tagesschau (2016): Putschversuch in der Türkei: Zusammenfassung der Ereignisse, ARD

Theoderich (2019): Portugal modernisiert Leopard 2A6. In: Doppeladler. Link: https://www.doppeladler.com/da/forum/viewtopic.php?t=920 [accessed August 2, 2020]

The London Gazette (1944): Wednesday, 20 December 1944. Link: https://www.thegazette.co.uk/London/issue/36849/supplement/5841 [accessed June 18, 2020]

The Telegraph (2016): Shocking video shows man 'run over' by two tanks during Turkey coup. Link: https://www.youtube.com/watch?v=QbXqvwZsCYo [accessed October 22, 2020]

Triebert, Christiaan (2016): "We've shot four people. Everything's fine." The Turkish Coup through the Eyes of its Plotters. In: Bellingcat. Link: https://www.bellingcat.com/news/mena/2016/07/24/the-turkey-coup-through-the-eyes-of-its-plotters/ [accessed October 19, 2020]

Triebert, Christiaan (2017): The Battle for Al-Bab: Verifying Euphrates Shield Vehicle Losses. In: Bellingcat. Link: https://www.bellingcat.com/news/mena/2017/02/12/battle-al-bab-verifying-turkish-military-vehicle-losses/ [accessed October 19, 2020]

Truffer, Patrick (2017): Härtetest für den Leopard 2 Panzer. In: Offiziere.ch. Link: https://www.offiziere.ch/?page_id=49 [accessed October 18, 2020]

Twigt, A. (2018): Digitale revolutie op rupsbanden. In: Defensiekrant 08. Link: https://magazines.defensie.nl/defensiekrant/2018/08/01_Leopard2_08 [accessed July 29, 2020]

Uffelmann, R. (undated): Mein Einsatz als stvKpChef der 3./vstkMechBtl 1 im 1. Deutschen Einsatzkontingent. In: Eder, M. (als Ed., 2019) [first published in 2000]: Dienen für den Frieden im Kosovo. Neuedition, HePeLo Verlag Golbet

Ulbrich, N. (2019): Modernisierte Leoparden für die Truppe. Link: https://www.bundeswehr.de/de/organisation/heer/aktuelles/bundeswehr-laesst-kampfpanzer-Leopard-modernisieren-160264 [accessed June 18, 2020]

United States of America Department of Defense (2014): Report on Progress Toward Security and Stability in Afghanistan. Link: https://web.archive.org/web/20141102000803/http://www.defense.gov/pubs/Oct2014_Report_Final.pdf [accessed June 18, 2020]

UNROCA (undated): Link: https://www.unroca.org/ [accessed August 2, 2020]

UNROCA (2020): Poland 2018. Link: https://www.unroca.org/poland/report/2018/ [accessed August 2, 2020]

Verboven, S. (2014): LE LÉOPARD TIRE SA RÉVÉRENCE. Link: https://www.mil.be/fr/article/le-Leopard-tire-sa-reverence [accessed June 22, 2020]

Verlag Jochen Vollert (2015): Tankograd 5058 Kampfpanzer LEOPARD 2A7 Bester Panzer der Welt – Entwicklungsgeschichte und Technik Broschüre. 1. Edition, Verlag Jochen Vollert – Tankograd

Veterans Affair Canada (2019): Canada in Afghanistan - Fallen Canadian Armed Forces Members. Link: https://www.veterans.gc.ca/eng/remembrance/history/canadian-armed-forces/afghanistan-remembered/fallen?filterYr=2002 [accessed August 8, 2020]

ViralTimeLapse (2015) [footage is much older, presumably from the 1980s]: German engineering at its finest. Auf: Youtube.com Link: https://www.youtube.com/watch?v=zYI6gOc-3vQ [accessed November 15, 2020]

Vogel, T (2015): Die Wehrmacht: Struktur, Entwicklung, Einsatz. Link: https://www.bpb.de/geschichte/deutsche-geschichte/der-zweite-weltkrieg/199406/die-wehrmacht-struktur-entwicklung-einsatz [accessed June 10, 2020]

Von Manstein, E (1991) [first published in 1955]: Verlorene Siege. 12. Edition, Bernhard & Graefe

Von Seeckt, H. (2013) [first published in 1929]: Gedanken eines Soldaten. 1. Edition, tradition

Vollert, J. (2018a): HEDI und die anderen "Freikorps-A7V". In: Militärfahrzeug —Internationales Fachmagazin für Militärfahrzeugfans Fahrzeugbesitzer und Modellbauer, Issue 1-2018. Verlag Jochen Vollert – Tankograd

Vollert, J. (2018b): Eine kurze Geschichte des Panther. In: Militärfahrzeug —Internationales Fachmagazin für Militärfahrzeugfans Fahrzeugbesitzer und Modellbauer, Issue 1-2018. Verlag Jochen Vollert – Tankograd

Wallace, M (2007): Leopard Tanks and the Deadly Dilemmas of the Canadian Mission to Afghanistan. In: Canadian Centre for Policy Alternatives Foreign Policy Series, Volume 2, Number 1, February 2007

Weber, T. (2011): Hitlers erster Krieg: Der Gefreite Hitler im Weltkrieg – Mythos und Wahrheit. 1. Edition, Propyläen Verlag

Wiegold, T. (2015a): Aufrüstung in Norwegen: Modernisierung der Panzer. In: Augen geradeaus! Link: https://augengeradeaus.net/2015/04/aufruestung-in-norwegen-modernisierung-der-panzer/ [accessed August 1, 2020]

Wiegold, T. (2015b): Deutsch-Niederländische Zusammenarbeit – Panzer für die Landmacht, Standort für Deutschland. In: Augen geradeaus! Link: https://augengeradeaus.net/2015/09/deutsch-niederlaendische-zusammenarbeit-panzer-fuer-die-landmacht-standort-fuer-deutschland/ [accessed Juli 28, 2020]

Wiegold, T. (2016a): Panzer für die Niederländer, ein Schiff (teilweise) für die Bundeswehr. In: Augen geradeaus! Link: https://augengeradeaus.net/2016/02/panzer-fuer-die-niederlaender-ein-schiff-teilweise-fuer-die-bundeswehr/ [accessed Juli 28, 2020]

Wiegold, T. (2016b): Der Bundeswehreinsatz in Afghanistan. In: Bundeszentrale für politische Bildung.Link: https://www.bpb.de/politik/grundfragen/deutsche-verteidigungspolitik/238332/afghanistan-einsatz [accessed June 26, 2020]

Wiegold, T. (2019): Viereinhalb Jahre nach dem Abschied von der Großgeräte-Liste: Erster modernisierter Leo übergeben. In. Augen geradeaus! Link: https://augengeradeaus.net/2019/10/viereinhalb-jahre-nach-dem-abschied-von-der-grossgeraete-liste-erster-modernisierter-leo-uebergeben/comment-page-1/ [accessed Juli 29, 2020] (beachte hier auch die Kommentare zum Artikel)

Wikipédia (undated): 1er régiment de guides (Belgique). Link: https://fr.wikipedia.org/wiki/1er_r%C3%A9giment_de_guides_(Belgique)#1960-1994 [accessed September 27, 2020]

Windsor, L. et al. (2008): Kandahar Tour – The Turning Point in Canada's Afghan Mission. Gregg Centre for the Study of War and Society, John Wiley & Sons Canada

Yeo, M. (2019): German documents reveal Singapore received more Leopard 2 tanks. In: DefenseNews. Link: https://www.defensenews.com/land/2019/02/21/german-documents-reveal-singapore-received-more-Leopard-2-tanks/ [accessed August 2, 2020]

Zwilling, R. (2018a): Der Kampfpanzer Leopard 2 im Dienste der Bundeswehr. In: Militärfahrzeug – Internationales Fachmagazin für Militärfahrzeugfans Fahrzeugbesitzer und Modellbauer, Issue 1-2018. Verlag Jochen Vollert – Tankograd

Zwilling, R. (2018b): Leopard 2A5 Entwicklung, Technik und Einsatz – Teil 1. In: Tankograd – Militärfahrzeug Spezial N° 5075. Verlag Jochen Vollert – Tankograd

Zwilling, R. (2020): Leopard 2A4 Teil 1 – Entwicklung und Einsatz. In: Tankograd – Militärfahrzeug Spezia N° 5083. Verlag Jochen Vollert – Tankograd

K&F Verlag is a label of the EK-2 Publishing GmbH

Friedensstraße 12
47228 Duisburg
Register court: Duisburg
Register court ID: HRB 30321
CEO: Monika Münstermann

E-Mail: info@ek2-publishing.com

Cover design: Ff_designs
Author: Jill Marc Münstermann
Translation: Jill Marc Münstermann
Afterword: Thomas Antonsen
Cover design: Monika Münstermann
Used photos: AV7 = Everett Collection, Leopard 1 A5 and Leopard 2 A6 = film factory, Danish Leopard 2 in Afghanistan and Danish UN Leopard = Thomas Antonsen, Anders Fridberg, Kim Vibe Michelsen (Copyright Danish Defence Command)

1st edition, January 2021

ISBN Print: 978-3-96403-114-3
ISBN E-Book: 978-3-96403-115-0

Made in the USA
Monee, IL
19 January 2022

89340748R00066